# THE CHILDHOOD OF FAMOUS AMERICANS SERIES

. . . continued on next page

By DOROTHEA J. SNOW

**Eli Whitney:** Boy Mechanic
**John Paul Jones:** Salt-Water Boy
**Raphael Semmes:** Tidewater Boy
**Samuel Morse:** Inquisitive Boy

By WILLIAM O. STEELE

**John Sevier:** Pioneer Boy
**Francis Marion:** Young Swamp Fox

By AUGUSTA STEVENSON

**Abe Lincoln:** Frontier Boy
**Ben Franklin:** Printer's Boy
**Andy Jackson:** Boy Soldier
**George Washington:** Boy Leader
**Daniel Boone:** Boy Hunter
**Sam Houston:** Boy Chieftain
**George Carver:** Boy Scientist
**Kit Carson:** Boy Trapper
**Paul Revere:** Boy of Old Boston
**Clara Barton:** Girl Nurse
**U. S. Grant:** Young Horseman
**Buffalo Bill:** Boy of the Plains
**Anthony Wayne:** Daring Boy
**Myles Standish:** Adventurous Boy
**Booker T. Washington:** Ambitious Boy
**Wilbur and Orville Wright:** Boys with Wings
**Molly Pitcher:** Girl Patriot
**Zeb Pike:** Boy Traveler
**Nancy Hanks:** Kentucky Girl
**Tecumseh:** Shawnee Boy
**Sitting Bull:** Dakota Boy
**Virginia Dare:** Mystery Girl

By GUERNSEY VAN RIPER, JR.

**Lou Gehrig:** Boy of the Sand Lots
**Will Rogers:** Young Cowboy
**Knute Rockne:** Young Athlete

By GUERNSEY VAN RIPER, JR.—cont.

**Babe Ruth:** Baseball Boy
**Jim Thorpe:** Indian Athlete

By JEAN BROWN WAGONER

**Louisa Alcott:** Girl of Old Boston
**Jane Addams:** Little Lame Girl
**Julia Ward Howe:** Girl of Old New York
**Martha Washington:** Girl of Old Virginia
**Abigail Adams:** A Girl of Colonial Days
**Jessie Frémont:** Girl of Capitol Hill

By ANN SPENCE WARNER

**Narcissa Whitman:** Pioneer Girl

By ANN WEIL

**John Quincy Adams:** Boy Patriot
**Franklin Roosevelt:**
   Boy of the Four Freedoms
**Betsy Ross:** Girl of Old Philadelphia

By MABEL CLELAND WIDDEMER

**Washington Irving:** Boy of Old New York
**Aleck Bell:** Ingenious Boy
**Harriet Beecher Stowe:** Connecticut Girl
**Peter Stuyvesant:** Boy with Wooden Shoes

By KATHARINE E. WILKIE

**Zack Taylor:** Young Rough and Ready
**Will Clark:** Boy in Buckskins
**Mary Todd Lincoln:** Girl of the Bluegrass
**George Rogers Clark:**
   Boy of the Old Northwest

By ELLEN WILSON

**Ernie Pyle:** Boy from Back Home

By GERTRUDE HECKER WINDERS

**James Fenimore Cooper:**
   Leatherstocking Boy
**Jim Bowie:** Boy with a Hunting Knife
**Ethan Allen:** Green Mountain Boy
**Jim Bridger:** Mountain Boy

# Dan Beard

## *Boy Scout*

BY

Miriam E. Mason

ILLUSTRATED BY

Paul Laune

## THE BOBBS-MERRILL COMPANY, INC.
### *Publishers*

INDIANAPOLIS                    NEW YORK

This book is proudly dedicated
to
Den 5, Pack 432
Cub Scouts of
Silver Spring, Maryland

# ACKNOWLEDGMENT

THE author wishes to express her indebtedness to these books and persons who helped in some way to make Dan Beard seem very real and alive: *Hardly a Man Is Now Alive,* by Dan Beard, published by Doubleday, Doran & Company, Inc.; *Handbook for Boys,* published by the Boy Scouts of America; Lex Lucas, Director, Editorial Service, Boy Scouts of America, who kindly read the manuscript and helped me especially with the last chapter; Daniel B. Beard, Everglades National Park, Homestead, Florida; Leo Dinman, Librarian, Morley Library, Painesville, Ohio; Rebecca E. Cox, Librarian, Public Library of Covington, Kentucky; Mary Downing, Reference Librarian, Cincinnati Public Library; the Indiana State Library, Indianapolis, Indiana.

# CONTENTS

# LIST OF FULL-PAGE ILLUSTRATIONS

# DAN BEARD

*Boy Scout*

# I

## A CAMPFIRE IS MAGIC

### 1. *When the Rattlesnake Calls*

D AN BEARD was sleeping very soundly. Suddenly, just a few feet away from his pillow, there came a thin, dry, rattling sound.

Instantly Dan was awake. He bounced upright in bed. Then he stuck his head out the open window as far as he could lean without falling. His eyes were watchful and alert. His ears were listening.

"It's the rattlesnake," he muttered to himself. "It calls, and I am ready."

Dan, acting the keen-eyed mountain lion, peered cautiously this way and that through the pale-gray morning.

He saw nothing unusual. There was the well house in Mr. Mosher's back yard, with the big

11

wooden bucket on its curb. There were his mother's rosebushes covered with flowers. There was the apple tree in which robins and vireos lived.

There, too, close enough for him to touch, was the thick bridal-wreath bush. And again from its shelter came that piercing rattle.

This time Dan answered with a call of his own. "Helejah! Helejah! Helejah!" he cried softly. "Helejah!" It was the cry of the mountain lion.

At once the flowering branches of the bridal-wreath bush parted. Framed in dainty white blossoms was the freckled face of Dan's best friend, Harvey, who lived back in Big Creek Hollow.

"Ready to start?" Harvey whispered excitedly. His round cheeks were red with joy. His eyes were sparkling. For good measure he shook the snake rattles again.

Harvey shook the snake rattles.

"Gosh, Danny, don't they make a pretty noise?
You wouldn't know them from a real snake!
They woke you up in time, didn't they?"

"A mountain lion wakes in a hurry, anyway,"
Dan answered. "Are you sure it's really morning, though?"

It seemed very quiet all around. There was no sound of anybody stirring in the house, not even Margaret, the Irish hired girl.

"Sure. It's been morning a long time. The town clock was striking four when I came by."

"Well, I'd better get up. We've got lots of things to do today—hunting that Indian magic."

It was Dan's birthday, June 21, 1857. He was seven, and his mother had told him that he might spend the day doing what he wanted most to do.

It had not been hard for Dan to decide. What he most wanted to do was to spend the day with his friend Harvey. They would take a long walk. First they would go through the fields and woods hunting for Indian charms and woodland magic. Then they would walk along the Grand River and climb a hill that overlooked Lake Erie.

A day that began at four o'clock was not a bit too long for all the interesting things that might happen. Painesville, Ohio, in the summer of 1857, was Dan's idea of heaven.

He began to dress in a rush. Harvey slipped back under the shelter of the bridal-wreath bush and waited patiently.

Dan's clean clothes were laid out carefully on a chair. The water pitcher, well filled, stood by the washbowl.

Dan frowned as he looked at them. "I wish I didn't have to take so much time washing and dressing," he said to himself. "If I was like Harvey I could just start off in any old clothes, with the dirt still on my face. Then I'd have more time to spend in the woods."

After all, it *was* his birthday and he *was* seven. Besides, it was so early that nobody was going to notice his clothes or his face.

Dan put on a castoff shirt that had once belonged to his older brother Harry. Then he slipped into a pair of ragged old trousers.

"I'll be out in a minute. Helejah! Helejah!" he called softly to Harvey.

Barefooted, he ran noiselessly through the kitchen. He gave a running jump out the door and landed right on the tail of old Timothy, the family cat.

Timothy screeched in outrage and yanked his long, slippery tail out from under Dan's bare foot. Down went Dan against the big copper kettle. It was filled with rain water which Margaret had caught in day-before-yesterday's shower.

The kettle clanged down the steps with a great splash of water. It drenched Dan and Timothy alike. It roused Brownie, the sleeping dog, to wild excitement. It wakened several drowsy chickens perched in a pear tree.

Their uproar brought Harvey running from the bridal-wreath bush. His snake rattles clicked fiercely. Margaret, who slept next to the kitchen,

Dan landed right on old Timothy's tail.

roused also and came tearing out in nightcap and gown.

"Indeed, and I thought it was goblins or banshees!" the girl shrieked. She was astonished to see only two small boys staring meekly at her. "What might you be doing out at this hour of the night?"

"It's morning, and it's my birthday, and we're going to the woods to hunt magic," Dan explained. The rain water streamed off him.

"But first you'll go back upstairs and get yourself into clean, dry clothes," Margaret scolded fondly. "Then you'll come back down and eat yourself the good breakfast I'll cook for you. Then you'll sit yourself down and wait while I pack you a fine picnic meal. You can't be starving on your birthday!"

There was no use trying to argue with the determined Margaret, so Dan went back upstairs and got into clean clothes. He scoured his face and polished his cheeks to a fine rose color.

Dan invited Harvey to have breakfast with him. The hearty meal which Margaret prepared tasted good to the boys. Before they had finished eating, Dan's mother and father came in to say "Happy birthday, Danny!"

"Here's your birthday present," said Dan's father. He gave his son a small knife with a handle in the shape of a running dog. "When you've learned how to use this well, you'll get a sharp barlow knife," Mr. Beard promised.

Dan's eyes sparkled. How rich he was with a knife of his own! Now he would really feel like a scout as he walked through the woods. He was thankful to old Timothy for getting in his way and delaying him.

Mrs. Beard helped Margaret pack the food in a lunch basket. It was a very grand meal, with ham and chicken, sausage rolls, a small meat pie and several kinds of cake and fruit.

## 2. *The Young Scouts*

Old Brownie, the dog, wanted to go along with them, but Dan ordered him back. "He gets so excited he barks at everything," said the young scout. "We want to go through the woods like Indians, without a sound."

"Anyhow, he's likely to get into our lunch basket," Harvey said. He looked with interest at the hamper.

The boys felt they were well equipped for a long trip. Dan had his new knife, and Harvey had an old broken one with part of one blade. There was food enough in the basket to keep them from starving for several days.

Of course Harvey had his snake rattles, which were supposed to be magic. They would also be useful in scaring away any enemies the boys might meet.

"If wild animals or mean people come along,

we can hide behind a tree," Dan suggested. "You can shake the snake rattles hard, and they'll think a rattlesnake is there. Then they'll run."

The boys had an empty grain sack which they intended to fill with magic charms and treasure from the woods.

"Of course real old-fashioned scouts like Dan'l Boone and Timothy Tibbals wouldn't carry so much stuff with them," Dan said. They were walking now through the oak grove toward the deeper woods. "Real scouts can get along in the woods without much of anything. They get their own food and find their way without a path. They don't even need magic charms."

"After we've made a few more trips we can get along without so much, too," Harvey promised in a hopeful tone. Right now he was glad they were beginners and did not have to get their own food. Margaret's basket had a delicious smell.

Tall ferns grew in the shadows of the oak trees.

Dan set down the hamper and began searching beneath the tall fronds for the tiny brown curls that were hidden among the leaves.

"I'm hunting for fern seed," he explained. "Fern seed is magic. That's what Margaret told me. If you pick some fern seed and put it in your pocket, you're invisible. Nobody can see you. No animal, either."

"That would be handy if a big man-eatin' tiger came along, or maybe a fierce Indian huntin' scalps," Harvey said. He joined the search. "Or if just an old wild hog showed up, rootin' for acorns, I'd rather he couldn't see us."

Neither boy was sure what fern seed looked like. Margaret had neglected to describe it to them.

"We'll pick some of these little curly brown things and put them in our pockets. They must be what she meant." Dan gave Harvey a few and dropped some into his own trousers pockets. "I'm sure these will make us invisible to any ghosts or goblins or wicked spirits," he said.

The boys felt very safe. They went on through the oak grove, past the district school and the academy. They walked down the old Toll Road for a little way.

Dan and Harvey walked down the old Toll Road.

It was still so early that they met almost nobody. The world seemed to belong to them alone.
Only a few wagons, loaded with pigs and cattle
for the slaughterhouse, passed them.

"Want to ride, kids?" one friendly driver
called. But the boys refused.

"We're not tired. We *like* to walk," Dan explained.

Finally they came into the cool darkness of the
deep woods where their real hunt was to be. They
expected to find many treasures today. Most of
all, they were searching for a grizzly bear.

Harvey's grandfather said he remembered
when bears were thick among the wooded hills
of Lake County. "You watch close enough and
you may see one yet, sneakin' under the trees,"
the old man declared.

The boys had never seen any grizzly bears hiding around. They had not even seen any part of
a grizzly bear—bones or teeth or claws.

They were sure, however, that there must be something like that in the woods. "There's just bound to be a big tooth, or *something*," Dan had said often.

Wild animals were not the only interesting creatures which had been here when the pioneers came. There had been Indians then—Indian braves and hunters living in wigwams along the riverbank and by the lake.

Dan's uncles had told him many good stories about the Indian days and ways. Indians were great hunters, and they were great magic makers.

"Indians knew all kinds of magic," Dan told Harvey as the young make-believe pioneers walked through the woods. With his new running-dog knife he cut off a bunch of red berries and dropped them into the bag.

"That's right," Harvey agreed. He peeked under the fringed napkin of the lunch hamper to make sure everything was all right. "My grandpap knew an Indian chief who ate a whole grizzly bear every day."

Dan looked impressed. "Then I bet he was brave. Anybody who eats a grizzly bear gets as strong and brave as a grizzly bear. My Uncle William said so."

### 3. *Big Medicine*

"Let's sit down and rest awhile," Harvey suggested two or three hours later. The boys chose a big fallen tree that made a good seat.

They had walked a long way into the woods. They had walked up hills and down valleys. The long brown burlap bag was heavy with treasures which they had found.

"Big medicine," Dan said. He was looking into the bag with a pleased smile. "That's what the Indians call their magic charms," he explained.

Dan looked into the bag. "Big medicine," he said.

"My grandpap was friends with an Indian named Bow-Arrow," bragged Harvey. "It was the same Indian chief that ate a whole grizzly bear every day. Bow-Arrow had a thousand wigwams filled with big medicine!"

"We've got a good start, anyway," said Dan. In the burlap bag were several dried snakeskins, the skeleton of a squirrel, some Indian turnips, a number of eggshells and birds' feathers, red berries and pine cones. There were reddish stones which looked as if they might be magic, and some velvety moss. There were odd-looking old bones and some strange teeth.

"Funny we can't find hide or hair or bones of a grizzly." Harvey sighed. "Of course it might be that old Bow-Arrow took them all with him when he went to the happy hunting grounds."

Dan had an idea. It was very bold, but it was interesting. He pulled a dried-up bat's wing out of the treasure bag. "This looks like medicine.

I'm just sure it's magic. I'm going to wave it in the air and say a magic word and see if a grizzly bear comes."

"But suppose one does!" Harvey looked alarmed.

"We've got our fern seed in our pockets. The grizzly couldn't see us. And I'd like to see a real grizzly bear."

With an impressive motion Dan waved the old wing back and forth. He tried to remember Indian words which his Uncle William had told him. "Helejah! Bow-Arrow! Too-le-ze! Ashtabula!" he chanted solemnly. "Buffalo! Beaver! Rattlesnake! Crazy Weed!"

"Sh!" Harvey suddenly grabbed Dan's wrist. His grimy face grew pale. "It's workin', Danny! The magic medicine's workin'!"

No grizzly appeared in the shadows, but the boys heard a scratching movement directly beneath where they were sitting—and then a strange moan or growl.

"It's a grizzly all right!" Harvey gasped. "Let's get out of here!"

"But I—I want to see a grizzly." Dan's voice quavered. "I want to eat a grizzly and be brave and strong. He can't see us, can he?"

"Yes, he can!" Harvey wailed. He was fumbling in his pockets. "My fern seed's all gone. It must have leaked out of the holes in my pockets."

Dan discovered that his was gone, too. But he still had his running-dog knife. He opened the small blade. He muttered the cry of the mountain lion in a trembling voice. "Helejah! Helejah! Helejah! Shake your snake rattles, Harvey. That'll scare him!"

Now there was a violent scrambling in the big log. Bits of dust and punk flew from one end.

Any moment the boys expected to see a savage grizzly emerge from his long sleep.

"Come on! Let's climb a tree!" Harvey fairly dragged Dan after him. "That grizzly's hungry. He'll swallow you down in a flash."

Hand in hand the boys ran for a tree with low-hanging limbs. They climbed it quickly. It was not until they were settled high in it that they remembered the bag of big medicine, left behind in their rush.

High among the leaves, they could not see if the grizzly had come out. But they could hear scary noises. There were sounds of growling and tearing and chewing. The boys shivered.

"It's a big one, you can tell!" Harvey whispered. "Bet he's bigger 'n old Rajah, the circus elephant."

Dan felt cold with fear, but he had to see the grizzly. "I'm going to look!" he said after a good while.

Dan gazed toward the log with dread and curiosity.

Carefully he crawled down to a lower limb of the tree. He gazed toward the hollow log with mixed dread and curiosity.

There was no grizzly bear to be seen, but there was a very lean, lank, tan-and-brown dog sitting by the log. The lunch hamper, completely empty, was upside down at his feet. He was chewing the fringed napkin, and there was a happy look on his face.

"Not a grizzly after all!" Dan cried.

"Naw," Harvey said. "Just old Johnny Hawkins' shepherd dog Crawdad." A moment later he wailed, "And he's eaten up every single smidgen of our lunch, the old hog!"

Crawdad came to meet the boys. He wagged his tail in the friendliest way. His lean sides were bulging. His eyes had a look of love.

Dan couldn't help laughing. "Never mind," he said. "Perhaps Crawdad is a great spirit.

Anyway, I'm not sure but that I'd rather see him than a real grizzly."

"I just wish we'd eaten first," Harvey mourned. "Now, likely as not we may starve to death."

"It's a good chance for us to get our food as Dan'l Boone did," said Dan Beard. "Maybe that was Crawdad's idea—to test us."

He reached down suddenly to a place on the log. There, along with the burs and dust, the twigs and dry leaves and the soft old wood, was an exciting object. It was a great, long, curved claw which must have been imbedded in the tree years ago.

"It's a grizzly's claw!" Dan whispered. He held the object in his hand and looked at it with excitement. "We've found our big medicine, Harvey. My Uncle William says a grizzly's claw is the Indian's biggest medicine. We've found the magic charm we've been hunting!"

"We'd better hunt somethin' to eat," said Harvey. "Already my ribs are hittin' together."

Dan was not worried. Indeed he was glad for this great chance to prove himself a scout. He had his running-dog knife and his grizzly-bear charm.

Harvey had brought along a string and a pin. "Pioneer scouts can live for weeks on fish," he said confidently.

Followed by Crawdad, the boys walked on till they came to a stream. Their luck was good. Right away they caught a couple of small fish.

Dan scraped off the scales with his knife. He was proud. "Doesn't it make you hungry just to look at those fish?" he rejoiced.

"I was hungry already," Harvey admitted. "But how are we going to cook them?"

"When we get hungry enough we can eat the fish raw," Dan said. "Raw fish tastes real good when you're about to starve."

## 4. *The Real Magic*

"Shall we eat our fish now?" asked Dan a few hours later. It was afternoon. The woods were getting dusky.

"Let's wait till we get a little hungrier," Harvey said. He picked some wild raspberries from a bush and shared them with Dan. The boys had found several kinds of wild berries in the woods. They had found some water cress in a brook and some tender slippery-elm bark to chew. They weren't really starving.

Just then they heard the hail of familiar voices. Dan's three big brothers had come after them, but James, Harry and Frank didn't want the younger boys to know that.

"We just happened to be out here," said Harry, who was sixteen. "I was hunting butterflies for my collection, and James was sketching wild leaves. Wasn't it lucky we met?"

"We just happened to be out here," said Harry.

"We're going to enjoy those fish!" Frank smiled. He was a year younger than Harry. "Nothing better than fresh fish cooked over a campfire!"

"We just happened to bring along some bread and steaks," James said. He was the oldest of all, twenty.

The big boys found a wide, dry creek bed.

Carefully they laid a fire and lighted it with some sulphur matches. Soon the flames rose from the ground, clear and golden.

The older brothers roasted big slices of steak on the ends of long sticks. As Dan and Harvey cooked their fish over the flames they thought nothing had ever smelled so wonderful.

When they had eaten, all the boys sat for a time around the fire. Crawdad crouched humbly outside the circle.

"We'll wait for the moon to come up," James said. "It'll make the way home as bright as gaslight."

"You youngsters will probably be glad to rest awhile," said Frank. "If you want to, take a little nap before we start back."

But Dan did not want to take a nap. He wanted to watch the fire, warm and bright and beautiful in the darkness of the night.

The fire was like a living spirit, a magic spirit.

The fire *was* magic. Dan sat in the warm glow and thought over the adventures of the wonderful day.

"All day long I hunted magic, and here it is— in the campfire. The campfire makes you warm. It cooks your food. The campfire is full of pictures."

In the glow of the campfire the woods seemed to be alive with people. All about him Dan could imagine pioneers. He could almost see brave old Dan'l Boone fighting bears in the forest. He could see Timothy Tibbals, the wilderness scout. Simon Kenton was there too, and Kit Carson.

Rather sleepily Dan squeezed the magic claw in his hand. He wished to be brave and strong like the grizzly bear.

Now he began to feel brave and strong. In the light of the campfire he was not afraid of anything. When he looked hard he could even imagine that old Dan'l Boone smiled at him.

"You got along all right, didn't you?" said
Dan'l Boone, the scout, though the words seemed
to come from James's mouth.

"I'll do better next time," Dan promised

Old Dan'l Boone smiled at Dan.

eagerly. "And I want to learn how to start a campfire—a real Indian campfire—without matches."

Harry said, "There's the first star just coming out. Make a wish on it and the wish will come true."

"I've got my wish!" said Danny. He had wished to find magic and he *had* found magic. A campfire was magic, the finest magic in the world. He would never forget that as long as he lived.

## II

## PICTURE WRITING

ALL SUMMER the boys worked hard in learning how to start a campfire the Indian way, without matches. It was not an easy thing to do. You had to have just the right kindling, and you had to know just when to blow on the spark that fell from the flint.

But Dan did not forget his secret promise to old Dan'l Boone that night in the woods. He kept on trying until he saw his little fire blaze into life. It was a great victory.

Of course his fire was not built in wild country—just down by the creek behind the orchard. Then, too, the green corn ears which he and Harvey roasted were somewhat burned and charred.

All the same, the corn tasted delicious. When

the boys finished their feast they made a record
of it on a big flat sandstone. They found colored
rock and blue clay. Dan drew a picture of the
campfire and the roasted corn ears. Dan liked
to draw.

With their knives they scratched a few words
on the sandstone:

D. AND. H. BUILT CAMPFIRE
HERE. AUG. 29, 1857.

Both of them knew how Daniel Boone used to
keep records of what he had done in the woods
by writing on the trees. There was even a picture
in their schoolbook of the brave scout cutting
some words on a tree:

D. Boon cilled a bar here.

The boys sometimes laughed over Daniel's funny spelling. But they decided it was simply the scout's short and easy way.

"And anyhow," Harvey defended his hero, "a man that's smart enough to kill bears in the woods has got a right to spell however he wants to."

"Indians spelled mostly with pictures like this one." Dan added some red-stone flames to his campfire picture. "My Uncle William has traveled out west and seen Indian pictures made hundreds of years ago!"

The boys practiced trailmaking and pathfinding that summer.

"Making trails is a kind of picture writing," said Dan. "And finding paths is a kind of picture reading."

The boys made many trails. Sometimes the Mosher twins, Bob and Bert, went along with

them. Sometimes a crowd could be more fun
than just two.

The four boys could pretend to be a band of
pioneers, led by Timothy Tibbals or Dan'l
Boone. Or they could be a tribe of Indian war-
riors stealing silently through the woods.

Now and then they would be a pack of wolves.
They would track down their victim in the deep
shadows. Wolves, and all other wild animals,
were trailmakers and pathfinders, too.

When the Moshers' runaway cow went far
astray and the boys had to go hunt for her, it was
more exciting if they pretended to be a wolf pack.

"We're the wolves of the dark and bloody
wilderness," they said as they went out past the
barnyard. "Old Daisy is a hunted stag."

They trailed old Daisy, the desperate stag.
They searched the ground for her tracks. They
saw where she had kicked off the top rail of a

fence. They saw bits of hair where she had squeezed through a loose gate.

The old cow was shrewd. She would hide behind a bush or a patch of corn, hoping the boys would pass her by.

Old Daisy would hide from the boys.

But it was hard for even a smart old cow like Daisy to escape from sharp-eyed boys who were learning the ways of the wilderness. They always found her, no matter how far away she had wandered.

Once that summer when the boys had planned a fishing trip on the Grand River, Harvey failed to show up. The Mosher twins were disgusted. Harvey was the one who was going to guide them to the mud cat's hole.

"Harvey's just like his granddad, old Tobe," said Bob. "Can't count on him for anything."

Bert added, "Most likely he didn't want us to know where his old mud cat lives, anyhow."

Dan defended his friend. "You can trust Harvey," he insisted. "And he's not stingy, either. He's shown me the meadow lark's nest, and the honey tree, and the tanbark where the snake eggs hatch."

Bob and Bert wanted to go on without Harvey.

Their mother had packed a basket with ginger-
bread and apple turnovers. Their father had
given each of them a new fishing pole.

But Dan was loyal. "I'm going to find out,
anyhow. Maybe Harvey's hurt. Maybe he cut
off his leg splitting kindling. Maybe the house
burned down with him in it. Maybe he's been
carried away by gypsies."

The twins saw it was useless to argue with him.
They certainly didn't want to go on without Dan.

Grumbling, they followed him out of the barn
lot and down the road through Moody's Hollow
toward Big Creek. About halfway there was a
tall oak tree with a hollow place in the trunk.
This was the Signal Tree, where the boys sometimes left messages for one another.

Dan reached his hand into the tree. Sure
enough, there was a message. It was a piece of
brown butcher's paper with red spots drawn all

over it. Under the red spots was scrawled a word:
"Grandpap."

"What's he say?" the twins demanded. They
gazed at the message. "Looks like something
pretty awful!"

Dan grew rather pale. "I'm not exactly sure,
but I think he says his grandpap has got the
smallpox!"

"Whillikins! Let's hurry back home!" Bob
gasped.

Bert agreed. "Thunder, yes! I don't want to
get smallpox!"

Dan didn't want to get smallpox either. Smallpox, as anybody knew, was a horrible disease.
"But I can't desert Harvey!" he said. He pointed
to a black smear at the bottom of the message.
"This stands for great sorrow and trouble. It
means that Harvey needs help. I've got to go
help him."

The twins grumbled more loudly. Dan turned

on them angrily. "You can go back home. Or you can go fishing by yourselves. I'm going on!"

Months ago he and Harvey had made a vow of lasting friendship. Each had given the other a solemn promise to be a true friend as long as earth stood and trees grew.

Dan stalked on down Moody's Hollow. The twins watched him for a while. Finally they followed at a safe distance. "We won't get close enough to catch the smallpox—just close enough to see what happens," they decided. "And maybe we can help get Dan back home."

There had been another message on the letter. It was a circle with a sort of little tail on it. That meant: "Stop at the Signal Rock and blow on the hunting horn."

The Signal Rock was a big ledge sticking up from the ground. Hidden in its base was an old hunting horn. Harvey's grandfather had carried it on many a hunt, and he had given it to the boys.

It made a good signal in times like this one. Dan reached into the ledge and drew out the old horn. He blew on it with all his might. The call echoed over the hollow.

After a good while Harvey appeared. He was running as fast as he could. His face was red and streaked with grime. He looked worried.

Dan blew on the horn with all his might.

Dan hurried to meet him. "Is he dead yet—your grandpap? Is he dead of the smallpox yet?"

Harvey stared in bewilderment.

Dan waved the letter at him. "That's what the picture writing says, doesn't it? That your grandpap's got the smallpox bad, and you're sad and in great trouble . . . and to signal you from the Rock?"

Harvey looked at the letter and shook his head. "You didn't read it quite right. What I said is 'Grandpap has hired me out to Mr. Hudson to pick the potato bugs off his patch. I feel bad, but I can't help it!' "

Dan began to laugh. He signaled to the Mosher twins, who were waiting cautiously in the background. "Come on! It's not smallpox after all. It's only potato bugs!"

The four boys laughed till tears rolled down their cheeks.

"The idea of getting smallpox mixed up with

potato bugs!" Bob jeered. "Why, anybody could see that's a picture of potato bugs, not smallpox!"

But Harvey's laughter faded into distress. "Likely smallpox wouldn't have lasted half as long. Mr. Hudson's potato patch is as big as the world, almost. It'll take me from now till doomsday to pick off all the bugs."

Bert shrugged his shoulders. "Well, come on, Bob. Let's go back home." He smiled at Harvey. "We can still go on our fishin' trip when you get the bugs all off."

But Dan had another idea. "Who ever heard of a pioneer scout or an Indian brave or even a wolf leaving his brother in trouble? We'll *all* pick potato bugs!"

The Mosher twins began to protest. "Gee whillikins, my mother wouldn't like it if I earned money pickin' potato bugs from Mr. Hudson's patch!" Bob said.

"Anyhow, we don't need the money," Bert added.

Dan put his hands on his hips and surveyed his neighbors with an icy glare. "Who said anything about money? Friends don't help one another for money, but because they're friends! You boys come along and do your share. If you don't, I'll——" He thought hard. "If you don't, I'll have Margaret call old Chemosh and Dagon down after you some night."

This threat worked. Old Chemosh and Dagon were Irish goblins and very fierce. Margaret was always talking about them and their frightful actions.

But after the four boys started working they found potato-bug picking was not so bad. It became a game. The spotted bugs were enemy Indians trying to move in on a pioneer settlement. It was exciting to see which of the four scout fighters could capture the largest number of redskins.

On a beech tree at the end of the potato patch they carved out the record of the battle in Dan'l Boone spelling:

HERE WAS FOT THE GRATE WAR WITH THE REDS. WE ONE.

# III

## THE FIRE FIGHTERS

IT WAS a Saturday morning in November. Dan had finished his breakfast early. He and Harvey and the Mosher twins were going to the woods to gather nuts.

"It'll be a grand day for nut hunting," he told his sister Lina, who was two years younger than he. She watched him get ready. He folded a long burlap bag lengthwise and fastened it around his waist with a long thorn.

He made sure his knife was in his pocket and that his medicine bag was fastened to his belt. The medicine bag held a few Indian charms, a box of Margaret's homemade salve and a small piece of very hard dried beef. There were also a flint arrowhead and a wad of tinder.

"We don't *expect* to have any trouble, but it's

very important to be ready for it," Dan said wisely.

"Don't forget the buckeyes for Margaret and me," Lina reminded him. "They're very important, too!"

He knew, of course, that buckeyes were big brown nuts which grew on the horse-chestnut tree. They were not fit to eat, but many people thought they had magic powers. If Lina and Margaret wanted some, he'd get them.

Harvey and the twins were waiting out by the well. Each of them had a sack pinned around his waist, and a medicine bag.

They went through the oak grove in front of the school. The boys loved this grove and had named the trees. They had given each one an Indian name.

The nut trees were far beyond the oak grove, three or four miles from town. It was a good walk. The ground beneath them was covered with nuts. Before long each boy had all he could carry of walnuts, hickory nuts and little round hazelnuts.

They came to a butternut tree where the ground was covered with delicious, oblong nuts. Then they took time to hull all their nuts to make more room in the sacks.

At last, however, the sacks would not hold any more hulled nuts. The boys found their backs beginning to ache a little under the burden. They were ready to go home.

Suddenly Dan gave an exclamation of distress. "Oh my goodness!" He paused and looked around. "I forgot the buckeyes!"

Harvey sighed in relief. "Is that all? I thought maybe a snake had bit you or something."

"But I promised Lina I would bring her some buckeyes," Dan insisted. "Margaret is going to make her a magic necklace."

"Tell her you couldn't find any," Bob suggested.

Bert said helpfully, "Tell her the goblins had already got them."

"But that's not true," Dan said. "I didn't look. I just forgot. I know where the buckeye trees are, too. They're off there through the woods and across the creek."

"That's a good two miles. It's too far," the twins decided.

Even Harvey protested. "Great, sufferin' catfish, Dan, we can't walk that far with these big bags! Necklaces are girl stuff, anyway, and not important."

"I know it. And I don't even believe in charm necklaces—not much." Dan groaned. "But I promised. That makes it important."

He reminded the boys how Lina had faithfully fed his turtles and his cake of baby black snakes when he was sick in bed with the summer complaint.

"Besides, Margaret needs the buckeyes to make a love charm for herself so that new man at the tanyard will be her husband. She's *depending* on me."

"Well, I've got a sprained ankle," Bob said. "I'll sit here on the sacks and guard them for you while you go back for the buckeyes."

"I've got a sprained back," Bert whined, "but I'll help guard the nuts, too. Someone would be sure to steal them if you left them here."

"I've got a sore foot where a sharp stone went through that hole in my shoe, but I'll go with Dan anyhow," Harvey promised. "You fellows watch the nuts."

Harvey and Dan tramped over the long way toward the horse-chestnut trees. It seemed much longer now than it ever had before. Dan's back and arms ached. He wondered if it was a little silly to go to so much trouble just for girl stuff like a charm necklace.

But there was something restful about being in the woods. The boys walked along quietly. They enjoyed the clean woodsy smell. Squirrels ran briskly along the tree limbs. Cottontail rabbits stared saucily from the bushes.

After all, it was not too hard a trip to the tall horse-chestnut trees. Dan took his cap, which was long like a big stocking, and filled it with the shiny brown buckeyes.

Harvey had no such "toboggan cap." He took off his shirt. It made a useful carrying sack when the sleeves were tied shut. In a short time they had all they could carry.

Harvey said, "These are enough buckeyes to get a dozen husbands for Margaret and make a hundred magic necklaces for Lina—and a charm to keep off sickness besides."

The boys straightened up and started on their

homeward walk again. They would pick up the twins on the way.

"The woods smell good," said Harvey. He breathed deeply. "Seems to me the air smells better in the woods than 'most any place."

"I think so, too," Dan agreed. He took a deep breath. Then he sniffed quickly. "Say, Harvey, don't you smell smoke?"

Harvey breathed slowly. "Sure do. Smells like leaves burning—wood smoke!" He looked about in the gathering dusk. "This is a bad time of year for a woods fire. Everything's dry."

Dan looked around sharply. "Maybe somebody's got a campfire, cooking supper. But I think we ought to see."

"It might be tramps," Harvey said doubtfully. "Or maybe gypsies. Maybe it's even a murderer, hidin'."

"We'll walk like Indians," Dan said. "We know how to go through the woods without any sound. We'd better make sure about that fire."

Toeing-in as Indians would do, the boys silently followed their noses in the direction of the smoke.

Harvey was now as eager as Dan. "My grandpap remembers a time when a forest fire burned for two weeks," he whispered. "A forest fire's bad as a war, almost."

Finally they came in sight of the fire. There was nobody there, just a neglected fire. It was burning briskly in the November breeze.

"Somebody's gone off and left a cooking fire!" cried Dan. "The wind's blown the hot ashes around. Look!"

Several quick-running flames sprang from the dry leaves that surrounded the embers. They darted like bright snakes. A blazing leaf shot upward to start another fire a foot away.

"Gosh!" Harvey gasped. "Hadn't we better run, Dan? Woods fires are terrible. They can trap you like a tribe of Indians. My grandpap knew——"

"We've got to put out the fire," Dan said. "We're lucky, Harvey. There's the creek real close where we can get water."

"But what with?" wailed Harvey. "You can't carry much water in your hands."

"I've got a better idea anyhow," Dan panted. He set down his buckeyes and pulled off his shirt. "I'll soak this in water and beat out the blaze."

"Then I'll use my pants," Harvey offered. His old shirt was already filled with buckeye nuts. Clad in tattered old red underwear which had once belonged to his grandfather, he joined Dan in the fire fighting.

The boys soaked their garments in the creek water and pressed them down into the slender flames. Over and over they returned to the creek to dampen again these "weapons" for their fight.

Harvey joined Dan in the fire fighting.

When not a spark showed, Dan was still careful. "Fires are likely to jump up, even when you think they're dead," he said. "Likely those camp-ers thought their fire was out. We'd better be sure it is out now."

They carried wet mud and sand from the creek bottom and laid it over all the fire-blackened spots. Then they waited awhile to make sure no sparks came to life.

Their hands were blistered, and their faces were black. Harvey's long red underwear was streaked with smoke and creek mud. Dan's undershirt was torn and stained. There were long scratches and reddened spots on his arms.

"Gosh, you look funny!" said Dan, just as Harvey was saying, "Gee whillikins, you're a sight!"

They sat down to laugh awhile and to rest. In spite of their peculiar looks, their wounds and their tiredness, they felt good. They could not wear the shirt and the pants which they had used for fire fighting, for these were now blackened rags.

"We'll hang them up here on the tree, just as the Indians used to hang up the ears and tails and bones of the bears they killed," Dan said.

They tied the wet cloth into strong knots so the rags could not blow away.

"We've saved a lot of friends today," said Dan.

The boys gathered up their buckeyes and started home for the third time. The leafless branches of the trees rustled softly above them.

The Mosher twins were still keeping guard over the sacks of nuts. As Dan and Harvey appeared they shouted impatiently, "Hurry up! It's night, almost. What hap——"

They gulped and goggled as the fire fighters came close. "Wh-what happened to you?"

"Nothing much. Just a forest fire we had to put out," Dan said modestly. "We got our buck-eyes too."

"But you look awful!" Bob gasped. "Are you goin' to walk along the road like that? Your shirt's clear gone, Dan."

"And Harvey's in his underwear," Bert complained. "What would we do if we met some ladies on their way to the sewing bee?"

"Or the preacher—or Miss Collins, the teacher," Bob added with horror.

The twins were sure their mother would not want them to be seen with such strange-looking creatures.

"Then we'll have to think up a way to get Harvey home without being seen," Dan said. He tried to think of a plan. He wished he had some magic fern seed in his pocket. Any that had been there had been lost in the fight.

"I could stand here till it gets pitch-dark and then walk home," Harvey suggested dismally. "But I'd freeze stiff by then."

"Sure you would," Dan agreed. "Anyhow, a

person as brave as you doesn't deserve to freeze to death in his grandpap's old red underwear. We'll think of a better way. All think hard."

As they were trying to think, without much luck, they heard wheels going along the woods road.

Harvey crouched down among the nut sacks. "I'll hide here so they won't see me," he said. He was so cold his teeth chattered. "It might be some women."

"What if it is?" Dan cried boldly. "I'm not afraid of women. I've got a mother and two sisters. And I'm going to ask whoever's driving to stop and take Harvey to my house."

"I just know it's some women." Harvey shivered. "And they'll likely make me go to the Orphans' Home and wear a ruffled shirt and buttoned shoes."

But it was not women. It was a friendly-looking young man driving a small wagon filled with corn. He looked surprised when Dan hailed him. Then he listened with admiration to the story of the adventure.

"Get right in. Get right in, each and every one

"Get right in," the young man said.

of you," he said heartily. "I'm *proud* to give heroes like you a ride! My name is Wyman, Leo Wyman."

He looked at Harvey in his red underwear, and his eyes twinkled. "I've seen fine soldiers dressed in red uniforms," he said. "I've seen some of the finest soldiers in the world—French soldiers they were—wearing red uniforms. They remind me a lot of yours." He added, "They were called Zouaves, and I never saw anything handsomer than those red Zouave uniforms."

He dropped the Mosher boys at their house and drove on to Dan's.

Margaret was in the kitchen baking pumpkin pies when the nut hunters came in. She shrieked at the sight of Harvey and Dan. "What has happened now? Oh, great Chemosh and Dagon! What became of you?"

"We found our nuts, and we went back for the buckeyes, and we fought a forest fire and put

Dan and Harvey

it out, and we lost part of our clothes." Dan was very dignified but a little breathless.

"And you may well be proud of such brave lads," said Leo Wyman. He lugged in a sack of nuts.

tell their story.

Lina came running in. "Did you get our buckeyes? Did you get the buckeyes you promised for our necklaces and for Margaret's love charm?"

Dan and Harvey were proud that they could say yes.

Mrs. Beard came out and listened to the story. "You must both get cleaned up and have salve put on your wounds," she said. "Harvey may borrow some of Dan's clothes and stay for supper. Then we'll see that he gets back home safely."

Leo Wyman was as obliging as ever. "I'll be glad to wait until Harvey is ready to go home. I can take him back in my wagon," he offered.

"But what about your wife, your children, your family?" Margaret asked. "Think how anxious they'll be if you're late."

Leo Wyman shook his head sadly. He was a bachelor, he said. He had just come to Lake County and lived by himself. He was a carpenter.

"Then, of course, you must stay for supper with us," Mrs. Beard said kindly.

While the boys splashed and scoured themselves in the washroom they talked over their exciting adventure.

"It was lucky we went on for the buckeyes," Dan said. He looked out the window. The leafless trees were doing a brisk dance in the November wind. "By this time a lot of trees might have been killed."

Harvey agreed. He sniffed happily. Margaret's good cooking made the whole house smell appetizing. "Margaret's nice. She's a good cook. She *deserves* to have a buckeye for a love charm. Say, Dan, do you really believe buckeye charms are any good?"

"I don't know," Dan said. He thought of Margaret's rosy cheeks and pleased smiles when Leo had praised her pies. "I wouldn't exactly say they don't *ever* work. Anyhow, Margaret and Lina are happy because we kept our promise."

## IV

## HANDY-BOY DAN

### 1. *The Blunt-nosed Knife*

"DON'T you think I'm old enough to have a *real* knife instead of this little old running dog?" Dan asked one cold winter day.

Dan's father, James Henry Beard, was an artist. They were in his studio. It was a cozy place. A big log blazed on the hearth. It was pine wood and, while burning, it gave off a sweet forest smell.

"If I had a sharp knife, a barlow, I could do so *many* things," said Dan. "I could make presents for everyone in the family. I could make a breadboard for Mother, an apple-butter jar for Grandmother Beard, a dollhouse for Lina, a cradle for the baby."

A fierce gust of wind whirled against the windows and down the chimney.  Pine oil bubbled out of the log, and the flames turned blue.

"I could make a fine palette for you, too," he went on.  "I might even carve a paint-mixing bowl for you.  Perhaps it would be made of apple wood and decorated with the carving of a mountain lion or a black bear."

The artist smiled.  He crushed a bit of bright-red paint in the stone bowl which he had carved from sandstone.  He mixed the red paint with oil and stirred it with a small wooden paddle.

"Think of the time you would save if I had a sharp barlow knife," Dan said.  "I could cut the kindling.  I might even kill some animals and get fur for your brushes."

"A sharp knife is a fine thing if you know how to use it," the artist agreed as he stirred his paint.  He made nearly everything which he used in his painting.  He kept his paints in small bags made of fish bladders.  He made his own brushes of wild-animal fur.  He ground and mixed all his own colors in a stone bowl.  For this he used a stone pestle which he had carved.

"Then how soon may I have a sharp knife?" Dan asked.  He looked at the small knife which he had received for his seventh birthday.  "The running dog is so old and dull that he can only limp."  He laughed.

Dan's father laughed too.  He was a handsome man, with long curls which fell about his shoulders.  He wore a bright-red tie in a large bow. When he threw back his head and laughed he reminded Dan of a bold, handsome pirate.

"Remember what I told you about the Miami Indians?" the artist asked. "When the Miami boy was six or seven he got his first bow and arrows, but the arrows were blunt-nosed.  After he had learned to use his blunt-nosed arrows, he got sharp ones.

"First, though," Mr. Beard went on, "he had

"How soon may I have a sharp knife?" Dan asked.

to make the most of his blunt arrows. That is how he proved he was ready for sharp ones."

The artist laid down his bowl and pestle. He took Dan's running-dog knife and honed the dull blade until it had a little sharper edge. Then he gave it to his son, along with a piece of pine board which was lying on the floor.

"See what you can do with this," he said. He smiled again. "The Miami boy did not try to shoot deer with his blunt-nosed arrows. He frightened crows from the cornfield."

"Some of the windows rattle when the wind blows hard," Dan said. "I will pound little pegs between the sill and the frame. That will hold them tight."

He sharpened the wood into small wedges and pounded them tightly between the window sill and the frame. Then when the wind blew hard it could not get through or make the windows rattle.

"You are such a handy boy to have around,"
Mrs. Beard praised Dan.

## 2. *Signed in Blood*

Dan's favorite Christmas present that year was
a big book which his parents gave him. It was
named *The Young American's Picture Gallery,*
and it was made up mostly of pictures, with little
reading matter.

Each picture showed some great American
hero at a very exciting moment. Dan studied each
picture intently. Every time he looked at the
book he seemed to find something new and thrilling in the pictures.

There was a picture of William Penn making
promises of peace with the Indians. There was
brave George Washington by his campfire in
frozen Valley Forge. There was Daniel
Webster, the famous orator.

Dan liked the picture of William Penn especially. The great leader was smiling at the Indians in a friendly way. There was a look of trust on the Indians' faces.

"Friendship and trust are sometimes better weapons than guns or knives or arrows" was printed below the picture.

One Indian in the picture held a bit of earth with a twig stuck through it. The book explained that this was the old-time Indian way of showing the transfer, or sale, of land.

Dan's father told him some things which made the William Penn picture even more interesting. "When the Beards first came from England to Connecticut, they bought their land from the Indians by the old law of 'twig and turf.' The land they bought still belongs to the Beards."

The pictures of Francis Marion were exciting, too. They showed that hero of the Revolutionary War with his band of soldiers in the swamps.

Dan read that in the swamps they found their own food, slept beneath the trees and lived almost like Indians.

"When I grow up and buy a farm, I'm going to do it by the law of twig and turf, as William Penn did," Dan declared. "And if I'm ever a soldier, I want to be a swamp fox, just like Francis Marion!"

"Men really had to be tough in those days," said Dan's brother James. He looked up from the drawing pad on which he was sketching pine cones. "If they happened to be out of ink, they wrote their messages in blood—their own blood. Important agreements and promises were often written in blood."

"How'd they get the blood?" Dan wondered. "Wait till they got hurt, or something?"

"Certainly not," James answered as he inked in a line. "They slashed a finger."

From his corner Frank added, "Of course

only very special things were signed in blood."

Dan looked at the front page of the *Gallery*. His name had been written there in ink by his father. "Plain ink is not good enough for this book," he thought to himself. "This is a very special book and it must be signed in blood!"

That afternoon he waited until his father and the older boys were out of the house. The artist went hunting. The big boys took drawing pads and pencils and went out to make sketches of the animal tracks in the snow.

Dan went into the study with the book under his arm and his knife in his hand. Carefully he opened the book to a flyleaf. Then he got out his knife.

With his thumbnail he pinched the skin tight over his left index finger. He closed his eyes and slashed at the tip of his finger.

It seemed to him that he could feel blood gush out in a torrent. But when he opened his eyes there was no blood at all. The running-dog knife was too dull.

He tried again, this time with his eyes open, but it was like trying to cut with his thumbnail. All he could get was a little ridge on the end of his finger. It would take a long time to write a message in blood at this rate.

"Of course I could use red paint and *pretend* it was blood," Dan said to himself. Then he felt ashamed. Nobody ever did anything great by pretending or by choosing the easier way.

"I *will* sign it in blood!" he muttered. On his father's worktable lay James Henry Beard's barlow knife. It was sharp as a razor and silvery bright.

Dan seized it and drew the blade across his finger tip. This time blood flew out in a little fountain. Now it was like trying to write with a pen that had too much ink.

His finger smarted. He shook it impatiently.

Before he had time to write his name the door
opened and Margaret came in with her broom
and dustpan. She screamed at the sight of Dan.
"Oh, my poor boy! My poor brave laddie! Have
you hurt yourself bad? Sure, he's bleeding to
death, the brave lad!"

Margaret screamed at the sight of Dan.

She threw her cleaning tools to the floor and rushed out of the room and down the cellar steps. In the dimness of the stairs were festoons of cobwebs. She gathered a great handful of them. "This will stop the bleeding," she crooned. She swathed the cut with cobwebs, in spite of Dan's protests.

"Now come with me and I'll fix you something to eat. You're weak, I know, from so much bleeding. I'll make you an eggnog with cream and give you some sugar bread."

"But, Margaret——" began Dan once more. The girl paid him no attention, but dragged him off to the kitchen. There she covered his cobwebbed finger with a great towel bandage. She plied him with food.

Mrs. Beard came out to the kitchen. She looked with astonishment at Dan's heavily bandaged hand. She ran to him.

"The poor boy nearly cut his hand off!" Margaret explained. She would not allow Dan's mother to unwrap the wound. "He'll bleed to death for sure if you do! See how pale he is already! But brave—not a moan or a tear! Brave as Chemosh and Dagon, he is."

"I'd rather be as brave as an American, if you please," Dan corrected her. He felt rather heroic after all. He felt a little silly, too, because of the fuss they made over him.

He had no more chance to sign his name in blood. Margaret, Mrs. Beard and Lina surrounded him with their loving care. His father came home from hunting and went into his study to work. Dan had to go to bed with the book unsigned.

In the night he wakened. Silently he got out of bed and went down the stairs. He tore the big towel and the mat of cobwebs from his finger.

The blood was all dried up. He could hardly see the cut in the dim light from the fireplace. He squeezed hard, but could get only enough for one rather pale "D."

He sighed. "I'll have to try again." He made another little cut, but this time he made it carefully. "No use wasting blood," he said sensibly.

This time the blood came in a small amount, just right. He wrote in beautiful, rich, red letters:

# DAN BEARD'S BOOK

Then he went back to peaceful sleep. The book was properly signed now, signed in his own blood.

# V

# SPRINGTIME TRAILS

## 1. *When the Wild Goose Flies*

"WHEN YOU see the wild geese flyin' north you know it's spring," said Harvey.

The boys were going down the half-frozen lane which led toward the schoolhouse.

Dan stared up into the cold gray sky. "Looks as cold as Lake Erie up there now," he said. "Ground's cold, too. You'd need a big warm campfire today."

"This is only March," Harvey said. "First of March at that. But you can count on the wild geese just the same. No matter if the snowdrifts are tall as a man, it's still spring when the geese fly north."

"We'll be ready for it when it comes," Dan declared confidently.

The boys had spent many hours that winter planning what they would do when warm weather came. They had their medicine bags ready and their dull knives sharpened.

They had drawn several maps of the territory around them. When school was out they planned to do much exploring.

"All we need now is for the wild geese to give the sign," Dan said, and Harvey nodded agreement. "We must keep our ears open."

The day grew colder and more disagreeable. Miss Collins ordered the big boys to put more wood in the stove. "And since it is so dark in the schoolroom, we will not try to do our usual study from books. Instead, we will sing."

She decided that they would sing the "geography song." It was really a lesson, rather than a song. It was a way of reciting the states and their capitals.

"Massachusetts, Boston, on the Bay of Boston," droned the scholars. "State o' Maine, Augusta, on the Kennebec River."

Sleet drifted beneath the window sills. Some of the girls shivered and slid to the ends of their benches nearer the fire.

Suddenly, above the monotonous chanting of states and their capitals, Danny heard a new and more thrilling sound. He looked across the room at Harvey. Their lips shaped words to each other: "Is it?" . . . "It is!"

Dan jumped up from his seat. He ran to the door and threw it open so that he could look out. Cold air whirled into the room, and the big girls squealed in protest.

"It's spring!" Dan shouted. "I see them, up there—a great big flock!"

He stood on the schoolhouse step and gazed up into the gray sky. Against the tossing clouds the wild-geese flock moved north. They gave their wild booming cry. "Hear?" Dan did not

"It's spring!" Dan shouted.

heed the sleet on his face. "It's spring," he repeated. "The wild geese are never wrong!"

Miss Collins spoke sternly. "Come back to your seat, Daniel Beard! It may be spring for the wild geese, but it is the time of books for us! Take your pencil and slate and write this sentence twenty-five times: 'A schoolboy must not act like a goose!'"

Dan wrote his sentences carefully. He decorated the slate with pictures of wild geese flying across the sky.

For good measure he added a little to his task:

"Oh, the wild goose! The wild goose!
Up in the air so free and loose!
Wise as a scout and strong as a moose.
Oh, how I wish I could be a wild goose!"

Cold as that day was, the geese were right. Spring was really on the way. Soon the hyla, or tree frog, began its little piping down at the duck pond. Bullfrogs woke from sleep and practiced their bass choruses.

Dan and Harvey went on the first of their scouting trails. They carried no heavy lunch hamper this time, only some bread and bacon. They had learned well now how to build a fire.

They marked their trail in the Indian manner, with blazes cut on the trees, with bent twigs and other secret signs.

"But this is only the first one," Dan told Harvey happily as they sat by their campfire. "We're going on a thousand trails this summer. We're going to explore every place in the Western Reserve."

"What's the Western Reserve?" Harvey asked.

Dan was not sure, but he explained it as well as he knew how. "It's a great big piece of land that King Charles of England gave to some Connecticut men so they could settle it and build towns. Painesville is part of the Western Reserve. All Lake County is. My Grandfather Beard was a Connecticut man."

Harvey looked so impressed that Dan went on. He told him several of the adventures of Timothy Tibbals, the woodland scout who had led the Connecticut men safely through the wildest forests.

"Men had good times in those days." Harvey sighed. "If I could grow backward instead of forward, I'd like to grow into an old-time woodland scout, wouldn't you, Dan?"

"Yes, I would," Dan replied. He sharpened a forked stick for the bacon. "But even if the old times are gone, we can still do things the way they did."

Harvey piled dried bark and small bits of wood on the fire. It blazed up brightly. He blew on it to make it burn better. "An old-time scout wouldn't have to eat just bread and bacon, either, I bet," he said. "Any time he got extra hungry he could reach out and grab a wild turkey or a big fat deer." He smiled. "A big fat roasted rabbit would taste good, wouldn't it?"

"It sure would," Dan agreed enthusiastically.

The boys fastened their bacon to the forked sticks and held them over the blaze.

"I know just exactly how to roast a rabbit, too," Dan went on. "I read about it in a book on camping. First you take the skin off the rabbit and you take out the insides. Then you wrap the rabbit in good clean mud——"

"And bury it in the coals like a big roast tater," added Harvey. "Can't you just smell it there in the coals, Dan, gettin' brown and roasted?"

The young cooks were so interested in their make-believe rabbit that they forgot the bacon. It caught fire and blazed up in a flare of savory smoke. They looked ruefully at the charred cooking sticks.

"Now we'll have to go hunting—unless we

want plain bread," said Dan. "We're not so good as Timothy Tibbals yet. I bet he wouldn't let the bacon burn while he was thinking about roast turkey."

"I expect not," Harvey agreed. "But let's just toast the bread and eat it plain. We can make believe we've got meat with it. After that, maybe we'll feel strong enough to hunt a rabbit."

He added hopefully, "Unless, of course, you want to walk back home and get some more bacon, or maybe some leftover roast beef, at your house."

Dan shook his head sternly. "We're scouts, remember. We'll *hunt* what we eat!"

They ate their plain toasted bread and set off across a wide stretch of meadow. Although they looked sharply, they saw nothing that could be cooked.

"Don't know why all the rabbits and wild

turkeys have to hide just because we're hunting," Harvey complained.

Dan remembered some of the pictures of ducks which his father's friend Mr. Audubon had painted. "Let's go over to that big pile of brush and stuff that the creek washed up," he said. "Maybe there's a wild duck's nest there filled with eggs."

Harvey followed along without much hope. The boys tramped through the soggy grass toward the rubbish which had been left by spring floods.

"But it's not the season——" Harvey was saying when suddenly he stopped. "Look, Dan, there's something on the far side of the pile, down near the water."

"But what—?" Then Dan saw it. Both boys could see now what was struggling among the twisted brush and leaves.

"It's a *goose*—a wild goose!" Dan shouted in excitement.

Sure enough, it was a wild goose—probably one from the flock which had passed above the school building that day. It had become tired, perhaps, or been injured in some way. In any case it had fallen to the ground and found shelter in the pile of brush.

"Gee whillikins! A *goose!*" breathed Harvey. "A goose is better 'n a rabbit or a turkey or even a deer. A roast goose makes the best eatin' in the world!"

But the boys found that getting the goose would not be easy. The frightened creature crawled back into the very middle of the brush and gazed at them with its wild black eyes. It made hissing sounds, trying to scare them away.

They tried calling him, *"Chickie, chickie, chick!"* But he only drew farther back and continued to hiss at them. Their arms were not long enough to reach him from any direction. The driftwood was too firmly tangled to pull apart.

"Aw, let's give up," Harvey said at last in disgust. "What we need is a gun—only my grandpap won't let me use his."

"My father could soon get him with Old Baldface, his rifle," Dan said. He stared through the twigs at the wild goose. The goose stared back at him.

"My grandpap's a good shot, too. He could get him in a hurry," said Harvey. "Only trouble, though, he'd eat him all up too, without giving us anything but the neck."

Dan shook his head. "We've got to think up a way ourselves. Tim Tibbals and Dan'l Boone wouldn't expect their fathers and grandpaps to do their hunting for them."

"They likely had better weapons than we've got," Harvey said gloomily. "All we've got is my old beanshooter and our knives."

Dan thought hard. He tried to imagine what a real woodland scout would do in his place. One thing sure: a real scout would make use of what he had, even if it wasn't very good.

"You've got part of one blade on a knife and I've got my running dog. It's pretty sharp. We'll cut away part of the brush——"

"It will take forever," Harvey protested. "I'd rather just go home and eat salt pork."

Dan continued firmly: "Then you take your beanshooter and shoot at him enough to scare him out toward me. I'll catch him!"

The boys worked briskly for more than an hour. They hacked away at the twigs with their dull knives. They pulled at the twisted limbs until their backs ached and their hands were blistered.

But the plan worked. Finally they had made two openings. Each was big enough for Harvey to aim a pebble through it from his beanshooter.

He frightened the goose toward Dan's out-stretched arms.

"We've got him! We've got him!" Harvey panted as Dan at last held the big brown bird in his arms. "Gee-gosh, Dan, we're real scouts, aren't we? I bet Dan'l Boone couldn't have done better!"

"First time I was ever so close to a wild goose," Dan said. He held the bird gently, by its legs and around its body, so it couldn't escape. Its heart thudded wildly, and its black eyes had a glazed look. Dan could feel that its craw was flat and empty. It was light in weight. He could feel the bones under its feathers.

"He's thin now, but wait till we feed him up," Harvey planned eagerly. "Gee-gosh, Dan, my grandpap knows how to stuff a goose with onions and sage and bread and——"

Harvey's eager words broke off suddenly.

Dan held the goose gently.

"Look there, Dan! He's got a broken wing."
He gulped. "But I don't know if I really like
wild goose very well—to eat, that is. Do you,
Dan?"

Dan was stroking the feathers of the captive
bird gently. "I'm sure this one wouldn't be good
to eat. He'd be tough and stringy and, well,
wild!"

Harvey touched the goose with his grimy fin-
gers. "See how brave and proud he is, like an
Indian chief. He don't squawk as a pig or a
chicken would."

"That's because he's a wild goose," said Dan.
"Wild geese aren't meant to be roasted, I guess.
They were meant to be free and fly through the
sky."

"We'll keep it a secret," Harvey said. "We'll
hide him someplace and feed him and take care
of him and wait till his wing gets well. Then
we'll turn him loose, won't we, Dan?"

"We'll keep it a *deep* secret," Dan agreed. "We'll make a promise and write it on paper."

They found a hiding place for the goose in an old granary. Dan tied up the broken wing and the boys fed him well. Dan borrowed a sheet of drawing paper and wrote out a promise:

*We will not tell about the wild goose, but we will take care of him and let him go free when he is strong.*

Dan and Harvey had a special name for the time when they kept the wild goose. They called it "the wild-goose summer."

They spent hours pulling tender green grasses and plants from the meadow to feed the hungry bird. They dug angleworms and brought all sorts of vegetable foods to please their guest. They named him Traveler.

They wished they might tell the Mosher twins about Traveler, for they were proud of the beautiful bird. Besides, there was plenty of good grain in the Moshers' barn, and Traveler loved corn and wheat.

But they had made a vow not to tell about the goose, and they meant to keep their secret.

## 2. *The New Cub*

One day Dan and Harvey went down to the brook behind Dan's house to get a few minnows for Traveler. They just wanted to see what he would do with them. But when they got there they found a new boy sitting on the bank.

He was dressed up in a white suit, with a long belted blouse and long, girlish-looking pantaloons. His hair was as curly as the wigs on girls' Christmas dolls. He wore a silk tie with a big bowknot, white stockings and buttoned white shoes.

He was playing with a shiny red boat which

looked as if it had just come from a toy store. A popgun lay by his side.

"Whillikins!" Harvey muttered. "Who on earth's that?"

"Maybe he's lost from a traveling show or something," Dan guessed. He called across the stream, "What are you doing here, boy?"

"You get out of here!" the strange boy answered. "You get off this place. This is my father's farm!" He seized his gun from the ground. "You go in a hurry or I'll shoot you with this. It shoots pebbles and they can go right through you!"

Harvey dug into the edge of the creek and came up with a double handful of soft mud. He threw it with all his might. It landed in two big brown splashes on the spotless white suit.

But his violent motion made him lose his footing and he splashed face down into the water!

Harvey threw the mud at the boy.

"Goody, goody, goody! You're dead!" screamed the strange boy.

Harvey had gone down hard and banged his

head against a rock. He did not move. Dan jumped into the brook to help him.

The new boy seized his gun and began pelting Dan with small pebbles. "I'll kill you, too!" he cried. "And you can both get off my father's farm!"

Harvey sat up in a dazed way. Creek water was running down his face. He was smeared all over with mossy green mud. His nose was bleeding where he had hit the rock.

"You'd better both go. I'm dangerous!" cried the new boy in a trembling tone. He looked at the blood flowing from Harvey's nose. "Goody, goody——" he started, but suddenly changed his mind. "I didn't mean to kill you. Not really!"

He threw the shiny new gun into the creek. Without paying any attention to his fine clothes he jumped into the water. Then he began to mop Harvey's nose with the long white tail of his fancy blouse.

Harvey clenched his fists and for a minute looked angry. "Let me loose, Dan," he panted. "I'll drown him. I'll make him into a mud pie. I'll grind him into sausage."

Dan held his friend firmly. "Gee whillikins, Harvey! He's little. He's only a kid. And he's scared to death besides. You both look funnier than the clowns in Dan Rice's minstrel show!"

For an instant Harvey's face wavered between a scowl and a grin. The grin won. The fierceness disappeared from the new boy's face and he grinned back. Suddenly he plumped down into the water beside Dan and Harvey.

"My name's Rolla—Rolla Willoughby," he said. "I come from Cleveland. My folks bought the old Mentor house back there." He added, "There weren't any boys around where I lived. I thought I had to scare you or you might jump on me!"

"You're little and young," said Dan tolerantly. "I guess you're not old enough to know about William Penn, the Friendly Man, are you?"

Rolla shook his head. "No, he didn't live in Cleveland."

"He was the man who made peace with the Indians," Dan explained. "He said that friendship and trust are sometimes better weapons than guns and knives and arrows."

"I'd like to be friends with you," Rolla said timidly, "if you won't laugh at my clothes. My grandmother makes them for me."

"We'll try you out," Dan promised. "You've not made a very good start, but you didn't know any better."

The three boys made a promise of peace. The tail of Rolla's white blouse was their charter scroll. Each boy signed his initials in blood from Harvey's nose.

### 3. *Free Again*

Much as they liked Rolla now, Dan and Harry did not feel they could tell him about Traveler, any more than they could tell the Mosher twins.

The goose became plump and strong and quite tame. He had no use for minnows, but ate all the berries and seeds they gave him. When summer began to wane, Dan tore away part of the granary roof.

One frosty night he heard a thrilling sound: the cry of wild geese flying south. He sat up in bed and listened. He was sure that he heard an answering call from the old granary.

In the morning he found his guest was gone. The "wild-goose summer" was over. Only a couple of long feathers remained behind. Dan gave one to Harvey and kept the other for himself. They would not forget Traveler.

# VI

## BLACK WOLF PACK

### 1. *Old Enough To Be Trusted*

Now THERE were five boys to roam the hills and valleys, to explore along the Grand River and to build campfires for scout cooking.

At first the Mosher twins had not wanted to take Rolla into their gang.

"He's a sissy," declared Bob.

Bert agreed with this. "He's a sissy and stuck-up besides. And he's younger and littler than we are."

"Just because his father owns part of the ship-works down at the end of Dock Road he thinks he's big and important," Bob argued. "We can have a better time without him."

Dan was stubborn. "Let's give him a chance. Maybe he'll turn out all right."

114

"I'm sure he'd fight if any danger came along," Harvey declared. "He looks sissy with those girly clothes, but that's his grandmother's fault."

So the boys accepted Rolla, and Rolla tried as hard as he could to be a good member of the group.

This summer the boys called themselves the Black Wolf Pack. They had played being wolves before, but Uncle William gave them new ideas about it. He had just returned from a trip out west. He brought Dan a real wolfskin which had belonged to a Pawnee Indian in Nebraska Territory.

"Pawnee Indians are the most cunning of all scouts," Uncle William said. He held up the wolfskin so the boys could see its thick, dark fur. "A Pawnee warrior never traveled without his wolfskin. He used it for his animal disguise. He could imitate a wolf perfectly. When he walked among the lodges at night the people thought he was only one of the many wild wolves wandering about."

Uncle William got down on his hands and knees and threw the black wolfskin over him.

Uncle William threw the wolfskin over him.

He trotted around the back yard where the boys were sitting.

Brownie yelped in fright and ran under the house with his tail between his legs. Old Timothy spat fiercely. Then he scrambled up a tree as fast as his claws could pull him.

Even the boys felt scared. It didn't seem that it was just Uncle William under that black wolf-skin. He trotted over to the top of last year's potato hill and sat there. He turned his head here and there, seeming to sniff the air.

"But he's really looking over the village," Dan explained excitedly. "He's really an enemy, but nobody'll pay any attention to him. They'll take him for a plain old wolf."

None of the other boys had a real wolfskin which had been used by a Pawnee scout. But they managed to get something. Harvey went to the tannery and begged a calf's hide. Rolla's grandmother gave him a white bearskin rug. The

Mosher twins used the tanned skin of their old black mule. He had died long ago and his hide had been made into a carriage robe.

Of course it was too warm to wear the wolfskin disguises everywhere they went. Besides, the boys felt sure they could never be quite so skillful on their hands and knees as the Pawnee scouts were.

But they built a den for themselves back in the woods. They used old rails and the branches of trees. On the floor of their den they spread the buffalo robe which had been Uncle William's first gift to Dan.

They had good times in the secret den. Since he was the owner of a real wolfskin once worn by a Pawnee scout, Dan was Master of the Pack.

They decorated the den with feathers, picture writing and different kinds of bones and skins. Dan copied from his book the picture of William Penn and the Indians and hung it on the wall. They sat on their haunches on the buffalo robe, wearing their animal skins. They chewed dry grains of corn. Corn was important to the Pawnee Indians.

Every week they met and talked over their plans. Each Wolf was expected to do something special for the pack. The Wolf who did the greatest task got a long red feather. It was supposed to be an eagle feather.

Harvey won a red feather when he brought a big fish which he had caught in Lake Erie. The reward went to Dan when he made beds for everyone in the pack. For these he used pine needles, or "mountain goose," as they were called.

Bob Mosher won a red feather by shooting an arrow farther than any of the boys. Luckily the arrow hit and killed a cross old rooster sitting on the fence. The rooster furnished a fine feast for the pack, as well as many more "eagle" feathers.

Only Rolla, the cub of the pack, never did anything great enough to win the eagle-feather award. He tried hard, but all his tasks were outdone by the others.

Dan encouraged him. "You've got to keep on trying. Someday you'll do something big if you don't give up."

Each Wolf had his own bow and arrows. But there was one very special bow, with very special arrows. They were real Pawnee weapons. Uncle William had got them from a friend who was pioneering along the Platte River. The friend had traded a scarf to an Indian for them. Then he had given them to Uncle William as a gift.

The Pawnee bow even had a name. It was called "Protector of the Lodge."

"It's too big for you boys to use," Uncle William had said. "But it makes a good decoration for your wall."

"Protector of the Lodge" had killed many a

The bow was called "Protector of the Lodge."

buffalo, many a wolf, many an elk and many a panther in its Indian days.

"It's probably magic," said Dan. "Anybody that shoots with it will likely be a famous hunter."

Every week little Rolla looked longingly at the Pawnee bow and the arrows that hung beside it in a quiver. He had practiced and practiced with his own bow, but he had never brought in anything bigger than a barn rat. Even Timothy or Brownie would not eat the rat, so it was not worth much.

"If you'd let me take the Pawnee bow I'm *sure* I could get something," Rolla pleaded. "I might even shoot a pig that we could roast."

"You're not old enough to be trusted with the Protector yet," the older boys told him each week. "You keep on bringing candy and cakes from your grandmother. They make a good feast."

"But they're so *safe!*" Rolla wailed. "And

they'll never win me the red eagle feather for
greatness!"

## 2. *The Great Turtle*

Harvey's grandfather was a queer old man.
Some people thought he didn't amount to much,
for he was very lazy. The shack in Big Creek
Hollow where he lived with Harvey was about
the worst-looking house in Lake County.

Grandpap was a great teller of tall tales. Even
Margaret's Irish fairy tales were not so exciting
as Grandpap's stories. That was because everybody knew that Margaret's stories were fairy
stories. But nobody could be sure how much of
Grandpap's tales were true.

Most of the Painesville ladies did not like to
have their boys go to Grandpap's house. But the
boys often slipped down to the ramshackle hut
just the same.

They all liked Harvey and his collection of peculiar animals, snakes and bugs. He called these his "menagerie." And they loved to hear old Tobe Whipple tell tales as he whittled away on a pine stick.

The more exciting the tale became, the faster Grandpap whittled. Sometimes his pine stick would be nothing more than a toothpick at the most thrilling part of the story. Then every boy would eagerly hand him another pine stick so he could go on.

One hot, dry afternoon the Wolves decided to go wading in Big Creek. Afterward they went to Grandpap's house. He told them about the big turtle over in Bog Ore Swamp.

"It's a big snapper," he said. "It's as big as two or three whales and as fierce as a man-eating shark. It lives in the bottom of the swamp and comes up only when there's a heavy rain."

He told many more interesting things about

The more exciting the tale, the faster Grandpap whittled.

the snapping turtle. While he talked he whittled faster and faster. As it happened, he said, he himself had had several adventures with the great turtle. Once or twice he had almost shot him.

"Too bad I didn't, too!" He sighed. "The man who gets that turtle will go down in history along with Mike Fink, the river pirate. There's enough meat in that turtle to fill a dozen smokehouses. A turtle is mighty good eating—best in the world. There are seven kinds of meat in a turtle."

He began to tell the different ways to cook a turtle. All the boys listened intently.

Rolla was spellbound. His blue eyes were as round and wide as teacups. His mouth hung open. "Are you sure he's still there, down in the bottom of the swamp? Are you dead sure, Mr. Whipple?" he asked.

"Sure, I'm sure," Grandpap answered. "Nobody's ever caught him. He's bound to be there. He'll come up, soon as there's a good thunderstorm. He'll come to the top of the swamp, catch a few hundred barrels of fresh rain water in his mouth and eat up all the frogs and snakes in sight. Then he'll go back down to the bottom of the swamp."

"My!" Rolla sighed. "I'd like to see that big turtle when he comes up. I wonder why nobody ever got him."

"Nobody knows the secret," Grandpap said promptly. "I'm the only one who knows the secret. Bow-Arrow, the Indian chief, told me. But I'll tell you."

He paused long enough for five eager pairs of hands to supply him with fresh whittling wood. Then he solemnly told them the secret.

"Bow-Arrow said you have to be there just as it begins to rain. You have to watch till the old turtle sticks his nose up. Then you aim—*bang, wham*—right at his nose. If you can hit his nose before he has time to snap his shell shut, you've got him!"

"Do you suppose you could get him with a popgun—a real good popgun—I mean, if you hit him smack on the nose?" Rolla ventured.

The Mosher twins laughed loudly. "Imagine killing a turtle that big with a *popgun!* Why, a popgun won't even kill a bumblebee!"

"Happen you hit the turtle at the right place and the right time, even with a popgun, it might work," said old Tobe solemnly. "But Bow-Arrow always said the best thing was a good ashwood bow and a sharp flint arrow."

Rolla's eyes became a little wider, if possible. Then he jumped up. "Let's go home," he said suddenly. "I've got to take my Saturday bath."

Bob looked at the sky. "Anyhow, it's going to rain. We've got to pick the peas for dinner tomorrow."

Rolla did not say another word, but he seemed

to be in a great hurry. "I suppose he can't wait to get his Saturday bath," Bert said in a disgusted voice.

They came to the place where the road forked. Rolla almost ran up the lane toward the old Mentor house.

When Dan got home his three big brothers were there. They had been in Cincinnati for most of the summer. Dan soon forgot about Rolla and Old Man Whipple's tall tales.

When the promised thunderstorm began with its first drops of rain, Dan remembered that he had left his beloved *Picture Gallery* down in the shack. "Oh, dear, it'll be ruined if it gets rained on!"

He had even left the book open at the picture where Mrs. Motte was giving a bow and arrows to Francis Marion, the Swamp Fox. It was his favorite picture.

His older brothers had gone to singing school

over at the academy. His father and Uncle William were on a visit to Cleveland. His mother was upstairs reading to Lina while the baby, Adelia Bell, took a nap.

"Come on, Brownie." Dan whistled to the dog. But Brownie was afraid of thunder. He slunk away, whining, to hide in the woodhouse.

The wind was making things rattle in a ghostly way when Dan got to the shack. It crept beneath the buffalo rug and raised it high so that it looked altogether too lifelike. It seized the Pawnee wolfskin and made it do a weird war dance.

The book was lying open on the floor. Dan got one of the precious sulphur matches from the tin box on the wall. He lighted the tin lantern which Mr. Mosher had given the boys.

"Better take a look around and see that everything is all right," he said to himself. After all, he was the Master of the Pack. It was his duty to protect their property.

Then he noticed that the great bow and the quiver of arrows were gone. "Could they have blown away?" he asked himself. A crash of thunder almost split his eardrums. "No, that's not possible. They were hung to the wall on strong pegs and fastened with buckskin strings."

A flash of lightning made everything as bright as day. Dan could see that a log of wood had been rolled just beneath where the Protector had hung with the arrows beside it.

Now everything was clear to Dan. He knew exactly what had happened. Rolla had taken the Indian bow and arrows down from the wall. He had stood on the log to reach them. He had gone down to Bog Ore Swamp to get the big turtle!

No wonder Rolla had listened so intently. He had taken in every word. No wonder he had been in such a rush as soon as a storm cloud showed in the sky!

Dan was furious. "How could anybody be so

*crazy?* To go alone to Bog Ore Swamp in the evening! To believe everything Harvey's grandfather said!"

Rain swooshed through the cracks of the lodge. It was hard-driving, icy rain, and it was coming down harder every minute. The trees danced like witches. They waved their dark arms against the bright lightning.

Bog Ore Swamp was not a very safe place for anybody at any time. It was not really so much a swamp as it was a lazy low creek which never quite dried up. There was a deep dark hole in it where some iron ore had been dug out.

When it rained hard, however, the shallow creek rose up high and foamy-brown. Then it covered the road with rushing water.

Now that he thought of it, Dan remembered that a man had been drowned in Bog Ore Creek. He was driving a horse hitched to a cart, and the strong horse had been swept off its feet.

The hole where the turtle was supposed to live was on the other side of the creek. The water might have been shallow when Rolla crossed, but the rain would bring it up in a hurry.

Dan knew that he must go quickly. There wasn't time to try to get help. He had to cross the creek and reach Rolla before the water got too high. He covered his book with the buffalo rug and hurried out into the storm.

With the tin lantern in his hand he began to run down the lane that led to Bog Ore Swamp. The rain made him breathless, and the wind nearly knocked him off his feet. The lightning had a greenish color. Thunder roared, cracked and exploded with a sound like cannon.

But after he began to run Dan did not really feel afraid. The thunder and lightning, the wind and the rain and the swishing trees did not seem scary. They seemed almost like secret friends testing and trying him out. "Can you do it? Can you do it?" the storm voices shouted. And Dan kept saying to himself, "I can do it. I can do it."

Bog Ore Creek had flooded the road when he got there. It had a wild look as it tumbled along between wet, grassy banks.

But Dan knew that the water was not yet deep enough to be dangerous. He held his tin lantern high and splashed in. Once he stepped on a round stone and fell to his knees. But he had remembered to guard his light and was up again in an instant.

He began to call, "Rolla! Rolla!" There was no answer. Then he gave the secret call of the Wolf Pack: "Too-le-ze! Too-le-ze! Too-le-ze! Too-le-ze, Cub of the Wolf. It is the Master."

This time he heard a rather faint, wavering answer. "Too-le-ze! Here I am, Dan, over here by the Bog Hole."

"Don't move! Stay where you are!" Dan

shouted. He knew how dangerous a misstep would be.

Carefully he fought his way through the storm. There was a tree growing near the edge of Bog Ore Hole. The tiny ray of light from Dan's lantern showed Rolla sitting there. One arm was around the tree, but the other was holding the Pawnee bow and arrows.

"I'm w-watchin' for the big t-turtle," Rolla gasped. "He's just bound to come up tonight, don't you think, Dan?" He gulped. "I've swallowed a gallon of rain water myself, and—and I guess I was pretty scared, too."

Rolla sniffled. "I guess I'll never win the red eagle feather. I guess I'm not brave enough to be a Wolf, anyhow. I *tried* to get here soon enough. I ran all the way." He sniffed again. "My grandma thinks I'm staying all night with you."

"Well, that's so. You really are!" Now that he knew Rolla was safe, Dan was not worried

Dan fought his way

any more. They would sit the storm out together. Then when the creek went down they would go back home.

Dan suddenly felt very big and strong. He was nine years old and Rolla was only seven. It was his duty to look after the brave, foolish little cub.

through the storm.

"You and I are going to camp out tonight," Dan said cheerfully. "We'll find a better place than this, though. We'll go back there by that rock ledge. It will make a good windbreak."

"Don't you think it's kinda wet to sleep outdoors all night?" Rolla asked. He tried to sound brave.

Dan answered with loud cheerfulness. "This wouldn't be more than a spring shower to Dan'l Boone. He slept out in worse storms than this many a time. And think how famous he is!"

Now Dan was thankful for the miles of exploring which he and Harvey had covered. He was thankful that they had made maps of their travels. With his eyes shut he could remember the tall rock ledge which rose out of the ground beyond the bog.

"Isn't this a fine shelter?" Dan said when he and Rolla had reached the rock. "It's even rather dry on the underside. Why, you can just imagine a whole pack of wolves sleeping under this rock!"

In a few hours the thunderstorm wore out its fury. Rolla slept in the shelter of the rock. Dan took little cat naps. But it was a long, long night.

When morning came Bog Ore Creek was still much too high to cross. Dan climbed to the top of the rock and looked around. It was lucky they had moved to higher ground last night. The land where the rock stood was like an island. It was surrounded by water.

Dan wondered what an old-time scout would do. Why, he'd send up a signal, of course.

The thick tallow candle in the tin lantern was still burning. Dan hunted about for bits of moss, nutshells and pieces of wood which had been sheltered from the rain. Then he managed to light a fire on top of the rock.

How thankful he was for the hours he and the other Wolves had spent learning to make a smoke signal! A smoke signal could say, "In danger. Come." The greater the danger, the darker the smoke was supposed to be.

Rolla helped gather loads of green, damp stuff to lay on the fire when it started. The smoke rose up thick and dark.

Rolla and Dan sent up a smoke signal.

There was not much for breakfast.  A few dew-
berries and some slippery-elm bark gave the boys
something to chew on.

Rolla looked rather sadly at all the water
around him.  "I'll never grumble any more, no
matter how much breakfast my grandmother
makes me eat," he promised.  "I'll eat three bowls
of porridge every morning, and six slices of ham,
and four eggs, and a dish of fried potatoes, and
several pickles, and two kinds of pie, and lots of
tea with sugar and cream, and a whole pan of
sugar buns with strawberry preserves, and——"

This might have gone on for hours.  Dan's
mouth watered till he could hardly speak.  But
the recital was interrupted by a welcome sound.
"Look! Mr. Mosher...and Bob...and Bert...
and your brothers—all driving in a spring
wagon!" Rolla cried.

Then he gave a loud, excited shout.  "Look,

Dan, look! It's the *big turtle!* He came up after all!"

Crawling slowly out of the damp grass was a turtle about the size of a small butter bowl. It had a greenish shell and long greenish-brown legs. Its sharp, ill-tempered little face snapped at Rolla when the cub came near him.

But, after his night's adventures, it would take more than one little snapping turtle to scare Rolla. He took off his hat and slammed it down over the turtle. "I've got him!" he cried triumphantly. "I've *got* him!" He had forgotten the water, his hunger, even the horses, which were now splashing through the creek.

The other boys could not believe that Rolla's long-legged turtle was the giant of Bog Ore Hole. However, all agreed that he should have the red eagle feather of the week. He had certainly *tried* to get the big turtle. He had faced great dangers.

"Anyway, we need a turtle in our lodge," said Dan. "We'll put him in a wooden pail of water and he can sit at our council fire. We'll call him Little Turtle, Chief of the Miami."

Not long after this exciting night a wonderful thing happened. Dan's father called him into his study. "When the Indian boy was old enough to be trusted, he got sharp-pointed arrows in place of his blunt-nosed ones," the artist said. "You're old enough to be trusted, and you have earned your knife. I'm proud of you."

Dan could hardly speak. It was a beautiful barlow knife which his father laid in his hands. Its steel was like silver. Its blade was as sharp as a razor. It was long and dangerous-looking.

"It's a man's knife, Dan," his father said. "You have behaved yourself like a man. I'm not afraid to trust you with this knife."

# VII

## THE SONS OF DANIEL BOONE

### 1. *New Trails*

THE SHINY new barlow knife made outdoor trips twice as interesting. With its razor-sharp blade Dan could blaze signs on the hard bark of great trees in the deepest woods. He could carve records of exciting things which the Black Wolf Pack did.

After the adventure at Bog Ore Hole, the boys spent several other nights outdoors. They slept on beds of "mountain goose." If the Black Wolves could have had their own way, they would have lived outdoors day and night.

But Dan's father had news which would change these joys. "We're going to move back to Cincinnati," he announced one day. Cincinnati was the city where Dan and Lina had been born. Aunt Belle and Cousin Tom lived there.

The artist had many friends and interests in this Queen City. "It will be a better place for my work," he went on. "Besides, these are important times. The ill feeling between the North and the South of our country is getting stronger. Perhaps I could be more helpful if we lived in a city."

Dan was thunderstruck. This was very bad news to him. When he shut his eyes and thought hard he could remember Cincinnati. "The houses were close together and the yards were tiny," he recollected. "There were droves of pigs running around in the streets. I won't like it, I'm sure!"

He hated to think of leaving Painesville with its many joys. He could not take the menagerie with him to Cincinnati, nor the Black Wolf Den with its treasures. And where could he find friends like the Black Wolves?

Margaret wept and wailed at the parting. But she refused to leave Painesville for a new home in Cincinnati. "Here I was born and here I shall die!" she sobbed. "New ways and new places frighten me. I like the old and safe."

Dan looked at her sternly. Never would he let her know how much *he* felt like crying. He spoke brave words. "Scouts and pioneers were always moving," he said. "Hardly were they settled in one place before they had to go on. And think of the wild geese. They travel from zone to zone twice a year."

Dan did not feel quite so bad now at leaving Painesville. "We're going south, like the wild geese," he told his friends. All the same, he dreaded the thought of living in a city.

Their new home was a small cottage on John Street, one of Cincinnati's busiest streets. The yards there were tiny, just as Dan had remembered them. The houses were close together. He missed the wild pastures and near-by forest of Painesville.

But not far from his home was the beautiful Ohio River. Across from it rose the hills of Kentucky covered with woods.

"And I'm not a baby any more!" Dan realized with sudden joy. "I don't have to stay in the little yards as I did when I was three. I'm big and strong now. I know how to find my way around!"

"That's real Daniel Boone country," his father told Dan. He pointed across the wide river. "Those hills are the very ones he explored. These rivers—the Ohio, and the Licking over there in Kentucky—are the very ones he traveled."

"Do you suppose I can explore those hills?" Dan asked eagerly. "Can I blaze trails in the woods and travel in a dugout canoe?"

"Why not?" James Henry Beard laughed. "You have cousins over in Kentucky, Dan. Your Grandfather Carter was a flatboat captain on the

Ohio. Your Aunt May Carter lives near the Licking River. You're old enough to be trusted in Dan'l Boone's country!"

## 2. *The Sound of Tom-toms*

Dan loved the Ohio River. He liked to go down to the levee with Cousin Tom. They would watch the steamboats splash proudly up toward Pittsburgh or down toward New Orleans.

Dan enjoyed, too, a ride on the ferryboat which traveled between Cincinnati and the Kentucky side. The ferryboat man was old. He knew even more tales than Harvey's grandpap.

The old riverman liked to talk, and he often took Dan for free rides just so he could talk to him. "Wyandot Indians called the Ohio On-he-zuh-ye-an-da-wa," he said.

Dan practiced the long word till it came easily. "Onhezuhyeandawa. Onhezuhyeandawa! It's a beautiful name, and the river's beautiful," he said as he looked up and down the gentle wide river with its quiet ripples and peaceful curves.

"You haven't lived here long," said the riverman wisely. "When the rain falls for a long time it makes Onhezuhyeandawa cross. It wakes up the demons that live at the bottom of the river. They growl and show their teeth. Then they beat the tom-toms of war. The river rises and dances the war dance!"

"What about the people who live along the levee—over in Rat Row and on the Kentucky side?" Dan wondered.

The riverman shook his head grimly. "Onhezuhyeandawa carries them away, to the sound of the tom-toms and the growling of the demons," he said. "All who live on the river must learn to listen for the tom-toms."

Dan thought of old Mother Drygash, who lived on Rat Row with her pet bear, Adah

Mazeppa. She had once been a dancing fortune-teller in the circus which had winter quarters in Cincinnati. But she became too old and stiff to dance, and the fortunes she told were too sad to please the people.

The circus owner gave her Adah Mazeppa for her own. The bear had lost most of one foot in an accident, and she could no longer dance and do tricks either. The old bear and the old lady were good friends.

Mother Drygash did washing and ironing now, while Adah Mazeppa sat on the tiny front porch with one foot in the river. Now and then she caught a fish.

Dan was always glad to take his mother's laundry and go after it. He loved talking to Mother Drygash and hearing about her gay days in the circus.

"I hope the river will never wash Mother Drygash and her bear away," Dan said.

The boatman shook his head again. He looked grim. "When the tom-toms beat, you have to look out! Danger is coming. You must always listen."

Dan remembered the riverman's words. On rainy nights he sat up in bed listening closely for the sound of tom-toms. Next morning he would rush down to the river to see if it had risen and was doing the flood dance.

But the winter passed and the river stayed calm.

Dan's father was very busy these days, but he did not spend all his time painting portraits. He went to many political meetings and helped manage parades which marched through the streets of Cincinnati by torchlight.

Sometimes Dan would hear his father's friends talking in loud, serious voices. Two of those who came often were Mr. Lew Wallace, the lawyer from Indiana, and Mr. Salmon P. Chase, the governor of Ohio. The artist was painting a portrait of Governor Chase, but often they forgot about the portrait and sat talking.

Dan grew used to hear them speak of the Abraham Lincoln of Illinois, who had been born across the river in Kentucky. Would he be elected President?

"Can't you hear the tom-toms far away?" Mr. Wallace said one day. "I can. I can hear the drums of war in the distance."

"I wonder if I should tell Mother Drygash," Dan said to his father. He explained what the riverman had told him.

The artist laughed. "The river is low. That is Mr. Wallace's way of saying that we may have a war in our country. He was in the war with Mexico, you know."

On Dan's tenth birthday there was more family news.

"I think we had better move to Covington,"

the artist said. "In case there should be war between the states, there should be loyal Union men
in Kentucky."

Dan was glad to be going closer to the wooded
hills of Kentucky.

He bade a friendly good-by to Mother Drygash and Adah Mazeppa. He warned the old
lady to listen for the tom-toms of the river. He
gave her a large bucket of sorghum molasses for
a parting gift. Sorghum molasses was the bear's
favorite food.

Mother Drygash told Dan's fortune as a present. It was a good fortune. "You will become
great and famous," she prophesied. "I see you
in a high place, the leader of many thousands.
You will be loved and honored all over America."

Dan was amazed. He wondered if she thought
he would someday be President. "But she's pretty

old," he told himself. "She probably can't read palms very well any more."

When Dan told his mother about it, she laughed. "Why, Dan, nobody can foresee the future. Mother Drygash has probably said that to a hundred boys. But it's a good idea for you to try to fit yourself to be a great leader."

This sounded hard to Dan, but just now moving to Kentucky was enough good fortune anyway!

### 3. *The Young Rivermen*

Life in Covington was busy and interesting for all the Beard family, but most of all for Dan. Here the Licking River ran down from the hills to pour into the Ohio. On each side of it was a little town. Newport was across from Covington.

Dan soon made friends among the Covington boys. They were completely at home on the

Licking, and Dan fitted right into their games. They went swimming. They played flatboat on the piles of logs floating down to the sawmill. They fought with the Newport boys.

The river boys had their special heroes and hero stories. They knew endless tales about the outlaw Murrell, Mike Fink, the notorious flatboat bully, and the pirates of Cave-in-Rock.

Dan was able to add many true stories about his Grandfather Carter, who had been a boat captain on the Ohio. He talked a great deal about Daniel Boone, too. Soon the famous scout became the boys' favorite hero, taking the place of outlaws and pirates.

Partly because of Grandfather Carter, the boys looked up to Dan. They made him their leader.

They called themselves the Sons of Daniel Boone instead of the Covington River Rats or Mike Fink's Gang.

With their change of name and their new

leader, the boys found their interests changing, too.

It was more fun to be pioneers, exploring the wilderness up in the Kentucky hills, than to spend all the time in senseless fights with the Newport toughs. It was more exciting to go up the Licking River and roast potatoes over a campfire than it was to steal cigars from Laney's Shop and smoke them behind a barn. Besides, the roast potatoes did not make them sick!

Aunt May Carter lived about five miles up the Licking River on a creek called Bank Creek. Sometimes the Sons of Daniel Boone would go past her house. Then they would climb high on a hill which gave a wonderful view up and down the Ohio. From up there the river looked its most beautiful. The big steamboats going around the bends had a majestic appearance.

Sammy Kyle said, "When a fellow looks down and thinks about all the great Americans that

The Sons of Daniel Boone viewed the Ohio.

have traveled past here, it makes him want to be great too."

Late in January a winter freshet set the lazy little Licking on a wild "boom." Melted snow poured into the creeks and brooks that fed the Licking. The small river changed into a swollen brown torrent which rushed like mad into the Ohio.

The river "demons" woke from their sleep then. They growled and thundered and went on a wild rampage. Brown water covered the levees on both sides of the Ohio.

The Beards lived on high land and their home was not in danger. But Dan worried about Mother Drygash and Adah Mazeppa. "I hope she remembered to listen for the tom-toms," he said. "I hope she moved up on higher ground before the river reached Rat Row."

His parents were comforting. "Mother Drygash will be all right. The Cincinnati police went up and down the river warning people. They rescued many from the flood."

"I wish I could have been with them," Dan said. He looked out over the turbulent water.

"I wish I could go up and down in a boat help-ing people off the roofs and saving their lives!"

He decided that he and the other Sons of Dan-iel Boone should make a boat. Then when the next flood came, they would be ready.

"What if we don't have another flood for ten years," he said. "It's better to be ready ten years ahead of time than not be ready at all!"

# VIII

## THE BEAR

ON FEBRUARY twelfth Dan, his mother and sisters traveled across the river in the ferry-boat. The Ohio was calm again. They went to Aunt Belle's house.

Mr. Lincoln, the President-elect, was on his way to his inauguration at Washington. He was going to be in the Queen City on his birthday. There would be a parade on Mound Street.

"Will you go with us, Belle, and bring Tom?" Dan's mother asked. "It may be the only time the children will have a chance to see a President."

The two ladies with their sons and the two little girls had to wait a long time on Mound Street before the open carriage came rolling over the cobbles. The girls got tired and complained a little.

But Dan, always thrilled by heroes, was willing to stand all day just for a glimpse of the new President.

At first he was disappointed, for Mr. Lincoln's face was sad and gaunt. He sat awkwardly in the carriage. There was nothing dashing about him. "But he has a noble look!" Dan thought as the President's carriage came closer. He had climbed into a small tree to get a better view. He leaned forward as far as he could. The limb bent low and brought his eager face close to Mr. Lincoln's.

The President saw him and smiled. The smile gave Dan a strange thrill. He did not know why, but he felt as if he had a great honor and a great task given to him. He understood better now what his mother had said to him about being a leader.

He had a strong desire to go at once and do something noble, something helpful. He won-

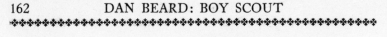

President Lincoln saw Dan and smiled.

dered what it might be, and he thought of Mother Drygash. He would go down to Rat Row and see how she was getting along. Perhaps she needed some kindling wood, or a hole mended in the roof of her shack.˙ He would stop at the store and buy a small pail of sorghum for her.

While the ladies were looking at pretty clothes in the shops, he hurried down to the levee.

Rat Row had been washed completely away. The small tumble-down shacks were gone. It took Dan quite a while to find his old friend. She lived now in a different house, farther back from the river. It was a much nicer house, provided by the generous circus owner. But Mother Drygash was not happy. Adah Mazeppa was lost!

She told Dan the sad story while tears rolled down her wrinkled cheeks. The little house had been flooded and was beginning to float down the river. Men had come and rescued her.

But they would not take the bear into the rescue boat. They said there was not room. Besides, the others in the boat were afraid of Adah Mazeppa.

"She's a good bear and very tame and gentle. She wouldn't hurt anybody. I begged them to

let me stay in the house and float down the river
with her, but they would not."

The little old lady sobbed harder than ever.
"That was weeks ago. The little bear will be
hungry. She will be cold. She will be lonely."

"Bears can get along by themselves," Dan
comforted her. "They're wild animals. They
can live in the woods and get their own food.
Their thick fur keeps them warm."

"Adah Mazeppa was lame. She never learned
to live in the woods." Tears fell faster and
splashed on the hot iron. "Worst of all, she
trusted me to look after her, and I deserted her.
I deserted her, Danny!"

Dan was troubled. He wondered what President Lincoln would say in a case like this, or
what Daniel Boone would do.

"I'm sure Adah Mazeppa will come back,"
he said, more bravely than he felt. He had seen

dozens of dead animals floating down the swift river. "Just have faith, Mother Drygash!"

The old lady looked up at him. Her dim eyes shone behind the tears. "You're a good boy, Danny, and I'll tell you a secret," she said in a low tone. "But first you must promise, on your honor, not to tell."

Dan promised, trying not to smile at the old lady's mysterious manner. She reminded him of his little sister, with her childish "secrets."

"I'm going to hunt Adah Mazeppa," said Mother Drygash. "I've asked everybody I know to look for her, but nobody will. They say she has run away and become wild again. They say she'd be dangerous, and they'd have to shoot her!"

"Won't it be hard for you to walk, Mother Drygash?" said Dan gently. The little old woman was bent and stiff with rheumatism. "I'll hunt for you. I'll look all around town."

She shook her head. "I've inquired everywhere. Even the police have looked. She's not in town. She has gone down the river, and *I'm going after her.*"

"But—but how?"

"You promised not to tell. Promise again, on your honor!"

Dan promised, and she told him in a whisper. She looked around her as though somebody might be trying to listen. "I have a boat. I rented it from Mr. Dunbar and did three washings and ironings to pay for it. I told him I wanted to go fishing. But I shall go down the river after Adah Mazeppa. I shall not come back until I find her!"

"Please, Mother Drygash, please don't go just yet. Wait awhile longer. I'll get my friends to help me. We'll all hunt for Adah Mazeppa. We'll look in the woods and the hills and all along Licking River and Bank Creek. I promise you."

The old lady looked into Dan's blue eyes. They

were honest and serious. He was not teasing her, she knew. He was not making empty promises.

"I'll wait then, a little while," she agreed. "I'll wait till you've had time to search before I go. But don't you tell my secret, Danny. They wouldn't let me go if they knew!"

Dan promised for the third time. He was thoughtful on the way home, for he felt that a burden had been laid on his shoulders.

He told the family about his promise to search for the lame bear. But he did not reveal the secret he had sworn to keep.

His mother shook her head sadly. "Dan, dear, you'll never find that bear. Poor old Mother Drygash is—well, she isn't quite right in her head any more. Old people sometimes get that way."

"Anyhow, if the bear is still alive, it's likely down in New Orleans by now," Cousin Tom said. "You won't find it along the Licking."

"You can't tell," Dan insisted. "She might

have got out on the Kentucky side and wandered up into the hills.  Anyway, I *promised* to look!"

## 2. *The Hunt*

The Sons of Daniel Boone joined willingly in the hunt for Adah Mazeppa.  None of them expected to find the little bear, but it gave them a good excuse for a trip to the woods.

They followed the Licking River out of town and through the wooded hills.  The flood had left many a pile of debris which would make a good hiding place for a bear.

The way became rougher and rougher as they went on.  The boys traveled slowly as they looked for tracks.  Cousin Tom had come over from Cincinnati. Sammy Kyle had brought his hound-dog Tinker to help with the search.  Tinker was interested and willing but not very useful.  He was always going off on wild trails, getting very excited.

His trails, however, led to nothing more than rabbits, squirrels, a few stray pigs and one bushy-tailed woodchuck.

"Let's leave the Licking here and follow the creek," Dan suggested. It flowed out of the deep woods, and its banks were wild and rugged. They were steep and tangled with underbrush.

Some of the boys objected because the going was so rough. But Dan was determined. "All the more reason why we should go that way. If you were a bear, trying to hide, wouldn't you choose the wildest place you could find?"

But no bear tracks appeared, and it was not very long before the boys were tired and hungry.

"Let's have something to eat," said Sammy. "Tinker's tired too."

"All right," said Dan. "This is a good camping place. Plenty of good seats and everything."

As he spoke, he brushed some debris off what looked like a big smooth log. Then he gave it a sharp glance. "Look, fellows, this is not just a log—it's a dugout canoe, a real log dugout!"

The others crowded about. Sure enough, there under a coating of mud and silt was the end of what looked like a dugout canoe. Dan hastily scraped mud from the wood with his knife. "It's gumwood, solid gumwood!" he cried excitedly. "That's what the Indians used!"

The canoe was upside down. It was securely anchored to the creek bank by driftwood and trash and a coating of half-dried mud. But it was beyond mistake a canoe, and it looked as though it might be at least twelve feet long.

It would take hours of work to dig the canoe out of the mud, but the boys could hardly wait to start. Hunger and fatigue were forgotten as they dragged away wood and trash and scraped at mud with their knives. After half an hour Bill Kelly panted, "I wish I had an ax."

"We need shovels too!" exclaimed Cousin Tom.

"We'll just have to stop and eat now," Dan said. "Then we can go home and get the tools we need."

"We can go back to Aunt May's," said Tom. "That won't take much time. She'll let us have an ax and spades and shovels."

"Good idea," cried the other boys. "Let's eat!"

It took the whole afternoon to uncover the dug-out. The boys dug and hacked and shoveled. They cut away tangled underbrush and at last pulled the canoe free from the heavy silt. Before they went home, each boy carved his initials on the boat. They pounded a stake deep into the mud and tied their handkerchiefs on it.

"In the name of Abraham Lincoln and Daniel Boone we take possession of this dugout," Dan said solemnly. "We promise on our honor to share it!"

"In our dugout canoe we can *really* travel," he thought happily. "Maybe we *will* find the bear."

The next day the boys were back on the creek bank early. The dugout was a beauty. It was twelve feet long, a solid gumwood log. They scraped off the last bit of mud and washed and scoured their treasure. They made paddles of driftwood boards.

It was a glorious moment when they finally pushed away from the creek bank and moved into the stream. Then they shot into Licking River and were on their way toward the Ohio.

Dan knelt at the prow, the others behind him. Now he felt a true son of Daniel Boone. He was in Boone country, on Boone water, and maybe even in a boat which had once carried the great scout!

They shot into Licking River.

A mile or so down the river they stopped at a farmhouse to get out of a shower.

"You can sleep in my barn tonight, if you're not afraid of the bear," offered the farmer. He grinned at their looks of astonishment. "You don't believe I've got a bear? Come out and look. I found it here when the flood went down."

Sure enough, it was the lost Adah Mazeppa. She recognized Dan and came limping over to him. She held up one paw like a friendly dog.

Dan told her story. The farmer looked doubtful and scratched his head. "I counted on making a rug out of this bear for my old woman's Christmas present," he said. "It'd make a nice warm rug for cold weather."

Dan had a blanket in the canoe. It took the blanket and all the money the boys had to buy Adah Mazeppa back.

But they could not begrudge the price. After all, they really owed their boat to the bear.

Mother Drygash received her pet lovingly. Tears of happiness rolled down her cheeks, but she did not seem surprised. "I was sure you'd find her, Danny," she declared. "You said you would hunt, and you're a boy who can be trusted!"

# IX

## WAR

IT WAS soon after the finding of the bear that war broke out between the North and the South. President Lincoln called for soldiers.

All three of Dan's big brothers joined the Union Army. Mr. Beard set about organizing a company of a hundred soldiers. He was a captain of cavalry.

The Sons of Daniel Boone changed their games to fit the times. They wore soldier uniforms which their mothers sewed up for them.

The Beards' house became "Fort Beard," and Tom called the farm "Camp Carter." Firing on Fort Sumter had started the war.

The boys built a fort with mud and wooden blocks. They fired pebbles at soldiers made of clothespins.

Dan's mother was busy helping with the Sanitary Fairs by which the ladies earned money to buy hospital supplies. The Sons of Daniel Boone helped, too. Dan made a model of a two-story log house. With its landscape it was three feet by a foot and a half. He carried it proudly to the Fair and it was sold for seven dollars and a half. Dan was becoming an artist like his father. The boys watered the cavalry horses and ran errands for the officers.

During that year and the next Covington was more and more like an army camp. Its citizens

The boys watered the cavalry horses.

were even governed by the army. Soldiers
marched back and forth. But there were no po-
licemen, no schoolteachers, not even citizens to
bother the boys. They still went fishing even
when the Confederates were on one side of a
creek and the Federals on the other. And they
still went camping.

Often in those war summers they would drag
the dugout onto one of the creeks that flowed
into Licking River and would paddle back into
the woods. They pretended they were hunting
for spies.

Dan was always the fire maker for the crowd.
He knew several ways of making a campfire
now. Sometimes he used the Creek Indian way—
rubbing a stick against a piece of dry wood.

Today, however, he had chosen the Blackfoot
way. He had lined the horn of a Texas steer with
damp, rotten wood. Then he had put in a big
live coal from his mother's kitchen stove.

On top of this coal he packed a piece of punk, or old wood, which he had found on a toadstool that grew only on birch trees. He closed the horn with a round piece of tin. The horn was airtight and the punk would smolder for a long time.

Each boy helped in some way. They gathered brush and wood and watched while Dan emptied his glowing fire horn onto the pile. The fire maker tended the blaze carefully until it was strong and bright.

Dick had brought three dozen eggs from his mother's henhouse. He wrapped each one in damp mud and buried it in the hot coals. "We won't eat 'em all tonight, but tomorrow they'll be good cold," he said.

There were potatoes and apples and corn to roast, too. Dan had even brought along a tin pail of succotash, his favorite food. This was to be a big feast. When it was eaten, the campers would get along on what they carried in their packs.

Dan was twelve now. He was strong and self-reliant.

"Let's tell stories while the supper cooks," one of the boys suggested. "Let's see who can tell the scariest one."

"I'll tell about Morgan, the raider," Tom offered. "It's a *true* story."

All the boys knew about Morgan, the Kentuckian who was a brave cavalry leader in the Southern army. They knew about his raids through the countryside. He seemed always to appear where he was least expected. Northern people shivered at the name of Morgan.

Tom made his story as scary as possible. Then he finished in a solemn way. "I've heard that Morgan and his men are coming up from Tennessee this very night," he said. "Their horses will rush through these very woods."

"You can't scare us." Sammy laughed.

"Horses couldn't rush through these woods. There's not room."

"They'd stumble over the brush and fall down," Dick Jones added. It was part of the game not to be frightened, no matter how much blood and thunder were in a tale.

Tom tried again. "Maybe they won't rush then. Maybe they'll slip through slow and soft. When Morgan gives the signal, his men will all shoot at once."

"We'd hear the horses," Dan argued. "We'd hear them breathe. We'd hear them stamp their feet and switch their tails."

"Morgan the raider has taught his horses to hold their breath," said Tom. "Even horseflies don't bother them."

"I'm still not scared," bragged Bill Kelly, whose father was a Cincinnati policeman. "My dad has told me just what to do if somebody shoots at me. First thing is: Don't run. Just stand up and——"

*Bang, bang, bang! Pop, crack, plunk!*

The sound of a dozen explosions burst suddenly into the dim quiet of the woods. Bill yelped in pain. "I'm shot! I'm shot!"

The boys, already a little nervous from the story, fled in all directions. Tom jumped into the water and crouched as low as he could.

Dan felt something sting him sharply on his cheek. He threw himself flat on the ground. He put his hand to his face, expecting to find it covered with blood.

But it was not blood that he scraped away. It was boiling-hot egg yolk, mixed with bits of dried mud and ashes from the fire.

Instantly Dan's quick mind told him what had happened. The eggs were exploding. He began to laugh. "You can all come out!" he called. "It's eggs! Nothing but eggs."

Dick admitted that he had not thought to make a tiny hole in each egg. The steam in the eggs caused them to explode.

"It's a good thing Dan kept *his* head," Tom said as he came like a mud turtle from his wet hiding place. "The rest of us would have been halfway back to Cincinnati by now, running like woods afire."

"And maybe leaving the woods afire, too," Dick said. "I was too scared to wait and put out the campfire."

Dan accepted their praise modestly. "I wasn't going to run away," he admitted. "I confess I was scared. But I wasn't going to run off and leave our dugout."

He scraped off a few bits of egg which had splashed against the prow of the boat.

"It would take more than Morgan and all his raiders to make me run away and leave our gum-wood dugout," he said.

# X

## UNCLE DAN OF THE BOY SCOUTS

IT WAS June 22, 1940. William Wayne, a Boy Scout who lived in a small Maryland town, was up very early that morning. It was his birthday, and he was thirteen.

But that was not the only important thing about this day. Bill talked about it to his little brother Jack, who also was up early.

"I'm going to see Dan Beard today," Bill said proudly as he dressed in his Scout uniform.

"Who's Dan Beard?" asked Jack.

"Oh, you'll hear all about him when you're a Scout," said Bill. "He's the National Scout Commissioner of the Boy Scouts of America."

Bill tied his neckerchief carefully. He made sure that his badges and insignia were properly adjusted and there was no dust on them.

"Dan Beard was ninety years old yesterday,"

he said. "Today there is a great celebration for him in New York. It will be a fine way for me to celebrate *my* birthday!"

Bill raised his right arm in order to admire the three merit badges which decorated it. One of them was for cooking, one for hiking and one for bird study. He wished he might have a chance to tell Dan Beard his adventures in winning those badges.

"When he was a boy Uncle Dan didn't have Scouting as we do, with troops and patrols and all. But he always loved the outdoors and outdoor fun. My, I'm glad he did! Just think what American boys might have missed if he hadn't loved pioneer ways and wanted to be a scout!"

Bill was ready now. The town clock struck five-thirty.

"I'd better get going," he said. His troop was to take the early-morning train for the New York World's Fair. The celebration for Uncle Dan

would be in the Hall of Peace, one of the most
beautiful buildings.

"Can't I go with you, just as far as the sta-
tion?" Jack pleaded. He had had his sixth birthday last December.

"Not this time, Jackie," said Bill. "I'll tell you
all about it when I get home. You can go when
you're older."

The New York train was packed today. "I've
heard that there'll be fifty thousand Boy Scouts
to see Dan Beard," his Scoutmaster said to Bill.

"Fifty thousand!" breathed Bill. "Fifty thousand boys all in one bunch! It'll be like a whole
city of boys!"

More and more boys got on the train as it
moved up to New York. There were Scouts of
many ages. There were groups of Cubs, not
much older than Jack. Many of them were
proudly wearing their Webelos emblems which
showed that they had passed their Tenderfoot

requirements. There were troops and troops of full-fledged Boy Scouts like Bill. And there were many Senior Scouts in their handsome uniforms, Explorer Scouts, Sea Scouts and Air Scouts.

The vast Hall of Peace was packed. Bill looked about him proudly. This was a great American Hall of Honor. Everything about the organization was American. American scouts and American Indians were its inspirations.

An excited hush fell upon the crowd. Eagerly everyone watched the platform, waiting for Dan Beard.

"Here he comes!" Bill whispered to his neighbor. A slim, wiry man in the uniform of a Scout walked to the center of the stage. It was the great Dan Beard. Bill's heart pounded.

The fifty thousand boys sprang to their feet. Their young, strong voices made a ringing chorus:

"Happy birthday to you!
   Happy birthday to you!
   Happy birthday, Uncle Dan!
   Happy birthday to you!"

The old Scout smiled at the young Scouts. He raised his hand again and again in the Scout greeting. It was hard to believe that he was ninety years old.

The singing faded away at last into the solemn words of the Scout Oath, led in the crisp, vigorous voice of Dan Beard:

"On my honor I will do my best:
   To do my duty to God and my country,
      and to obey the Scout Law;
   To help other people at all times;
   To keep myself physically strong,
      mentally awake, and morally straight."

Dan Beard was a favorite hero of the nation's boys. Most of those gathered in the Hall of Peace knew the story of his life and achievements, but everyone listened intently while the master of ceremonies told them once more.

"After he graduated from Worrall's Academy in Covington, Dan Beard became a surveyor along the Ohio.  He never lost his love of the outdoors and the ways of scouting.  He made pictures and wrote stories of outdoor life. His articles on camping were published in *St. Nicholas*."

"How well I remember them!" Bill's Scoutmaster said to the man sitting beside him. "Those articles and Dan Beard's books gave me a lasting interest in outdoor life."

The other man was a Neighborhood Commissioner of Troops.  He smiled and said, "I read *The American Boys' Handy Book* until it fell apart."

The master of ceremonies went on to say that Dan Beard had illustrated two of Mark Twain's books.  He had been a teacher of animal drawing in an art school and the editor of a magazine called *Recreation*.

"In this magazine," the speaker said, "Dan Beard ran a department for boys which was called Boy Pioneers, the Sons of Daniel Boone. Letters poured in and the department grew like wildfire. This made Dan Beard realize that almost every boy in the world has a natural love for the outdoors. He felt that the spirit of scouting is a fine one for boys to have."

Bill remembered how proud he had been when he became a Tenderfoot Scout and first repeated the Scout Oath, the twelve points of the Scout Law, the Scout Motto and the Scout Slogan.

"On February 8, 1910, the Boy Scouts of America were incorporated by a group of men who thought that the great game of Scouting would be good for American boys.

"Scouting was started in England in 1907 by Sir Robert Baden-Powell. Ernest Thompson Seton, a great naturalist, and Dan Beard joined forces to help make it really American.

"On June 15, 1916, Congress gave a Federal Charter to the Boy Scouts of America, with President Taft as Honorary President.

"So June is a great month for the Boy Scouts of America when they celebrate not only their Federal Charter but the birthday of Uncle Dan!"

The speaker sat down, and once more shouts and calls spread over the hall: "Hurrah for Uncle Dan! Happy Birthday, Uncle Dan! Hurrah, hurrah, hurrah!"

After the meeting the reporters crowded around Uncle Dan with their notebooks and pencils. Bill Wayne stood as close as he could. He was Scribe for his patrol. Perhaps he would hear something he should write down.

"What are your rules for health and long life, Uncle Dan?" one reporter asked.

Another added, "You seem as young and lively as any boy here, Uncle Dan. Can you explain your health and good spirits?"

Uncle Dan answered them in his brisk, short sentences. "My rules are simple. Here they are:

"Serve with sacrifice. Help everyone you can in all the ways you can.

"If you have work to do, do it *now*. Don't put off what needs to be done. Don't shirk.

"Don't worry. Smile. Smile, even if you feel like grumbling.

"Laugh it off; whether it's a slight, a disappointment or a tumble, laugh it off!

"Relax. Keep your head. Don't get excited over trifles.

"Get close to God. Then stay there. Be as faithful in your religious duties as in any others."

The reporters scribbled fast. Some of them took pictures. Bill Wayne wrote down Uncle Dan's rules, too.

Suddenly Dan noticed Bill's intense gaze. He smiled at the boy from Maryland. He held up his right hand in the Scout sign. Bill responded with the Scout salute to his leader. The old Scout and the young one stood like that for an instant. No words were spoken, but Bill Wayne felt that he had made a solemn promise.

"I'll keep on traveling the trail," he vowed silently. Now he was eager to go home. He had something to tell Jack. He would do a good turn for his little brother. He would help him get started in the Cub Scouts. Perhaps he could even be a Den Chief.

"It's been a wonderful day, Uncle Dan," said one of the reporters as he put his notebook away.

"So it has! So it has," returned Dan Beard. His eyes were following William Wayne when the young Scout walked away with his patrol. He smiled to himself as he got into the automobile which was waiting for him.

He knew there would always be pioneer trails winding into the wilderness. And there would always be brave young Scouts to follow them.